THE LOST VOICE
OF
QUEEN VICTORIA

THE SEARCH FOR THE
FIRST ROYAL RECORDING

by

PAUL TRITTON

ACADEMY BOOKS

The Lost Voice of Queen Victoria
The Search for the First Royal Recording
by Paul Tritton

First published in 1991 by Academy Books Limited

ISBN: 1 873361 11 4

Printed by:

Hobbs the Printers Limited
Southampton, Hampshire.

Published and distributed by:
Academy Books Limited
35 Pretoria Avenue
London E17 7DR

Direct sales enquiries to:
Telephone: 081 521 7647
Facsimile: 081 503 6655

To my mother and father.

A reproduction of the Bell-Tainter Graphophone, made for the Science Museum, London, by Mr D. M. Field using specifications and photographs supplied by the Museum of American History, Washington, DC.

CONTENTS

FOREWORD

It is a paradox that, while the voices of the most famous
Victorian poets, a prime minister, an actor, a musician and
other eminent people of those times have been preserved for
us, the voice of the Queen herself did not apparently survive
and her one well-documented official cylinder message was
broken on her instructions after being played. Most students
of sound history have been content in the knowledge that the
recorded legacy of the most famous 19th Century Briton was
a closed subject.

They had reckoned without the persistence of Paul Tritton
who, while researching a notable British engineer, Henry
Edmunds, found his tracks of enquiry leading to people with
connections in Royal circles just over 100 years ago. The
Edmunds trail also led to the engineer's friendship with
Thomas Edison and an interest in primitive phonographs,
and a number of pieces of a possible discovery started falling
into place. The search for the probable Victorian cylinder
reads like a detective story, with inevitable dead ends and the
going back to earlier fragile leads, and most urgently of all the
contacting of surviving generations of relatives of the principal players.

When the cylinder is actually found it proves to be a rare
early example of the first type that could be put on or taken
off the phonograph at will, and finding the right apparatus to
play it makes for further difficulties. How it comes to be
played and transcribed eventually is explained in detail.
Whereas getting these results was largely a team exercise,

what led to the playing of that cylinder was entirely due to the perseverance and tenacity of the author, who has at the same time become the historian of aspects of phonograph history that are still largely unexplored.

George L. Frow
President
City of London Phonograph and Gramophone Society

INTRODUCTION

The story that follows developed from an assignment I was given in 1980 while working as a freelance writer for the international house journal of Rolls-Royce Motors Ltd (now Rolls-Royce Motor Cars Ltd).

In 1979 the company had celebrated the 75th anniversary of the formation of the partnership between the Hon. Charles Rolls and Frederick Henry Royce, who went into business together to build and sell luxury motor cars. The man who introduced Rolls to Royce in the summer of 1904 and helped them to draw up their partnership agreement was Henry Edmunds, who in the 1870s had left his home town of Halifax, in the West Riding of Yorkshire, and embarked on an extraordinary career as an electrical and motoring pioneer. In 1906, at the opening of the factory that Rolls-Royce built in Derby to produce Silver Ghost motor cars, Henry Edmunds was flatteringly referred to as 'The Godfather of Rolls-Royce'. The 75th anniversary reawakened interest in the company's origins and founders, and it became evident that little was known about Henry's life before and after he brought Rolls and Royce together. David Preston, the editor of the Rolls-Royce Motors journal, commissioned me to research Henry's forgotten years and write an article about him.

In the 1920s, Henry wrote his own account of how he persuaded Rolls the motor dealer and Royce the motor engineer to pool their talents. Henry's reminiscences were published in the house journal of a Glasgow electrical engineering firm, Mavor & Coulson, and as this is the only surviving first-hand description of the first meeting between Rolls and Royce, it has been quoted in many books and articles on Rolls-Royce's early history. I found that Henry's article was only one of 20 by him entitled *Reminiscences of a Pioneer*, an evidently neglected source of 'I was there' recollections about the introduction of electric lighting, electric power, the telephone, the motor car - and the Phonograph. Henry's articles, and some unpublished documents that I obtained from his great grandson, Michael Pritchard, sent me off on the 'Edmunds trail' in several exciting and unexpected directions. I discovered so much that, after my article was published in the Rolls-Royce Motors journal in 1981, I decided to continue my research and write a book about this amazing man. What especially fascinated me were Henry's revelations that in 1877 he became a friend of Thomas Edison, the inventor of (among other things) the Phonograph, and that in 1888 he gave the first demonstration in Britain of the Bell-Tainter Graphophone, a rival to Edison's wax cylinder Phonograph.

Henry even claimed that Queen Victoria asked him to demonstrate the Graphophone to her and that on his behalf his associate, Sydney Morse, went to Balmoral and recorded the Queen's voice.

That claim, and the whereabouts or fate of the cylinder, had to be investigated. While I worked on my biography of Henry Edmunds the story of the 'Queen Victoria cylinder' took on a life of its own. The chapters that follow review Henry Edmunds's role in introducing the Phonograph and Graphophone into Britain, and the events leading up to and surrounding the recording of Queen Victoria's voice sometime in the late summer or autumn of 1888.

Finally I tell how I traced a cylinder that once belonged to Sydney Morse, and review the circumstantial and audible evidence that suggests that it could be a recording of a voice that those who are fascinated by the Victorian era and its inventions never expected to hear.

This book appears in advance of my biography of Henry Edmunds, 'The Godfather of Rolls-Royce.' This will be published in the Spring of 1992 by Academy Books and will report further on any additional information that comes to light about the cylinder and the mysterious voice embedded in its grooves.

Paul Tritton
Maidstone, England
November, 1991

PART ONE
'Mary had a little lamb'

Credit for the introduction of recorded sound into Great Britain must go to one forgotten pioneer, Henry Edmunds. He was born on March 20th, 1853, the son Henry Edmunds, Snr, a partner in the firm of Edmunds & Hookway, engineers and iron merchants in Halifax, in the West Riding of Yorkshire. His mother, Caroline, died some two months after his birth and he was brought up by his foster mother, Sarah Hannah Milnes. After attending a series of private schools until he was fifteen, the young Edmunds went to work for his father, displaying great promise as an engineer, and having a fascination with heat, light and power. At the age of eighteen he designed an oil engine, and in 1873 he and two friends patented an oil vapour lamp which could light or heat a cottage or generate steam for a marine or locomotive engine. This was the beginning of a lifelong career as an entrepreneur and engineer, and was the first of more than 150 inventions with which he was to be associated.

The series of adventures and experiences that led Henry Edmunds to become a sound recording pioneer began almost by accident. In 1877, a few weeks after his 24th birthday, he was working in his father's ironmongery business in Halifax when John Crossley, MP, a member of the family that owned the town's famous carpet making factory at Dean Clough Mill, called at the Edmunds's warehouse and asked Henry for some zinc plates for an electric battery. 'Certainly,' said Henry, 'would you like them plain or amalgamated?' Crossley was impressed by Henry's interest in lighting and power and invited him to attend the first demonstration in England of a new form of electric arc lighting called the 'Jablochkoff Candle'. The demonstration was staged on June 15th, 1877, at the West India Dock in

Henry Edmunds in 1877, the year in which he met Thomas Edison and heard his historic recording of 'Mary had a little lamb.'

London, and as he was leaving Henry met the inventor of a competitive arc light, Richard Werdermann, who persuaded him to go to New York - at his own expense - and introduce the Werdermann lamp into America.

Eight days later, Henry sailed from Liverpool with little more than a promise of fifty per cent of whatever he could earn from selling Werdermann's patents, and a letter of introduction to William Wallace of Ansonia, Connecticut, one of America's eminent electrical pioneers. Henry's venture was a failure but he stayed in America for several months and met many scientists and engineers who were friends of William Wallace, including Professor George Barker of the University of Pennsylvania and Thomas Edison, who were Wallace's guests during August.

Edison, 30 years old, was at this time entering the most productive phase of his career. He had spent the first ten years of his working life as a newsboy on the Grand Trunk Railway. These years had been amongst the most dramatic in his country's history, the American Civil War commencing only one year after he started work. He soon noticed that he sold many hundreds more copies of newspapers on days when they carried reports of major battles, so he started to make regular visits to the composing room of the Detroit *Free Press,* to read the headlines in advance of publication and decide whether the day's news was so important that he should collect extra copies. After seeing headlines announcing a battle in which there had been some 60,000 casualties, he arranged for brief advance bulletins to be telegraphed to the stations on his route and be chalked up on the platforms before his train arrived. This had a dramatic effect on his sales and, in 1862 he became a publisher in his own right, his *Grand Trunk Herald* being the first newspaper to be printed and issued from a railway train.

His next venture was *Paul Pry*, a periodical containing society news and gossip, but when the enraged subject of one of his more colourful stories threw him into a river, Edison decided to quit publishing and became a telegraph operator. In 1871, at the age of 24, Edison was appointed telegraph supervisor to the New York Gold and Stock Company. Anxious to find ways of increasing the capacity of the telegraph lines, he invented a system of quadruplex telegraphy, which transmitted four different signals simultaneously along the same wire. In 1877, the year after he became a full-time inventor, he began working on ways in which to improve the latest development in telecommunications, the telephone. The first telephone had been demonstrated by Johann Philipp Reis in 1860 but it was incapable of transmitting sustained articulate human speech. It was not until 1876 that this was achieved by Alexander Graham Bell. Edison recognized the fundamental importance - and the shortcomings - of Bell's telephone, and set to work to find ways of increasing the range and clarity of the instrument.

A few weeks before he had visited William Wallace, Edison had noticed, while experimenting with the telephone, that the diaphragm in its receiver vibrated to the sound of his voice. Being hard of hearing, he decided to test the strength of these vibrations by attaching a needle to the diaphragm and allowing it to prick his finger. He wondered whether the sound waves striking the diaphragm could be recorded, via the pin, as indentations on some form of moving medium, such a strip of paper or his "telegraph repeater". This was one of his latest inventions and took the form of a machine fitted with a rotating platen and paper disc. The dots and dashes of incoming telegraph messages were recorded as a series of indentations on the disc, which when played back on a similar machine re-transmitted the signals down another telegraph wire.

Watched by his assistant, Charles Batchelor, Edison tested his idea for recording sound waves by pulling a strip of paraffin-impregnated paper under a pin attached to a diaphragm, while at the same time shouting 'Halloo'. The paper was indented just as he predicted, and when he pulled it under another similar diaphragm he and Batchelor heard a distinct sound "which", wrote Edison, "a strong imagination might have translated into the original Halloo." He jotted down the details of the experiment in his laboratory notebook, adding the comment "There is no doubt I shall be able to store up and reproduce automatically at any time the human voice perfectly." Later, he turned to a blank page in his notebook, wrote the heading "Phonograph" at the top of the page, and drew a sketch of his invention; but he failed to foresee the most promising application for his discovery. All he wanted to do was to store and reproduce the sound of the human voice so that he could complement his 'telegraph repeater' with an instrument that would record and re-transmit telephone conversations.

It is surprising that at this vital stage in his experiments, Edison found time to go to see William Wallace. Edison had a reputation for working day and night on a new idea, pausing only to snatch a few hours' sleep when he became exhausted. Had he realized that he was on the verge of making a talking machine with applications in entertainment and education, rather than telephony, he would prob-

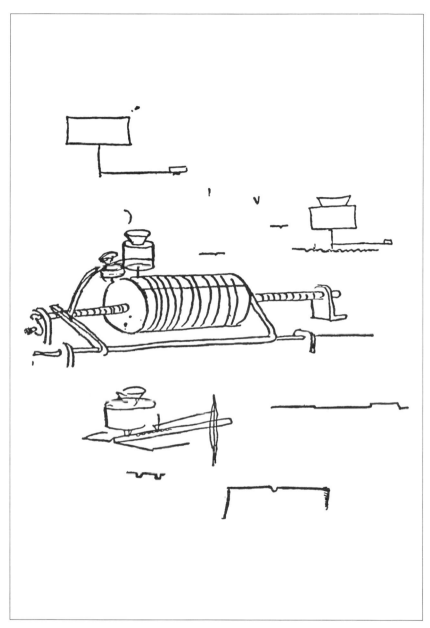

Edison's first sketch of the Phonograph.

ably have remained in his laboratory to develop a prototype capable of saying more than an indistinct 'Halloo.' But Edison, like Professor Barker and all the other visitors to Ansonia, wanted to see Wallace's latest invention, the 'Telemachon,' a dynamo and motor capable of transmitting electricity over long distances. The prospect of a cheap, clean and abundant form of energy to illuminate streets and buildings and drive industrial machinery was, in the summer of 1877, of much greater interest to Edison than recording and repeating telephone calls.

Henry Edmunds kept himself occupied in various ways in the months that followed his first meeting with Edison. There was work to do, promoting Werdermann's lamp and studying America's latest electrical inventions, but from the end of August he took several weeks off to go sight-seeing. He visited Niagara Falls and from there travelled to Chicago, Detroit, St Louis and Pittsburgh. From Pittsburgh he made a long journey by train and buggy to see a huge oil "gusher" that had erupted in deepest Pennsylvania. His next destinations were Washington, DC (where he had a conducted tour of the White House), Baltimore and Philadelphia, where he once again met Professor Barker. Henry returned to Ansonia in October, demonstrated the Werdermann lamp to the Academy of National Sciences at Columbia College, New York, on October 26th, and in November visited several factories and scientific institutes.

He then prepared to return home - empty handed, in one sense, since his efforts on Werdermann's behalf had been unsuccessful, but not entirely without any prospects for the future because Wallace had made him his European representative for the Wallace arc lighting system. Henry also took with him a pair of magneto telephones, designed by Alexander Graham Bell and made by William Wallace; Henry was also hoping to help promote the telephone in Britain. In *Reminiscences of a Pioneer* he described the climax of his visit to America;

> Before returning to Europe I called with Professor Barker one afternoon ... on Mr T.A. Edison, at his then small laboratory in Menlo Park. Prof. Barker led the way, opening the door; in a dimly lighted interior we could just see Mr Edison and his assistant, working upon a small brass cylinder covered with tinfoil. Edison held up his hand dramatically. We halted. He slowly turned the cylinder with a handle, and an unearthly metallic voice, with a strong American accent, spoke out the words Mary had a little lamb!
>
> We had just arrived in time to hear the first reproduction of mechanically recorded speech, and that piece of tinfoil was the parent of the Phonograph, Gramophone and all similar recording machines.

Henry gave another account of this event in a letter he wrote to a newspaper in 1927:

> I was in Mr Edison's laboratory with Professor Barker of Philadelphia when Mr Edison first recorded speech ... I was in New York when Professor Barker called and suggested we should take the train to Menlo, New Jersey, to see what Edison might be doing. We had both met him a few weeks earlier. When we arrived at the laboratory, a

wooden building, we both saw Edison, surrounded by his assistants, who put up their hands to warn us something was happening. We walked carefully to the table on which was a curious looking instrument with a brass cylinder covered with tinfoil that seemed grooved with curious indentations on the groove [sic], (and) a flywheel at one end of a steel shaft which, when we arrived, Mr Edison turned. Great was our astonishment when we heard the spoken words 'Mary had a little lamb.' Our astonishment was even greater than that of the other listeners, for evidently Mr Edison had spoken the words just before we entered the building and we had no idea what was coming. Thus we were just in time to be in at the birth of the Phonograph. I still have an original Phonograph sent me the year after by Mr Edison, which I treasure greatly.

More by luck than intention, Henry had been present at one of the most important moments in scientific history.

A few days later he left New York. He travelled to England almost as quickly as the news of Edison's amazing 'talking machine'. Edison had given him a letter of introduction to William H. Preece, chief electrician to the British Post Office, and although the letter was probably primarily intended to tell Preece about Edison's latest invention for the telephone, a carbon microphone, the Phonograph would surely have been mentioned.

In January 1878, Henry set up in business on his own account as an electrical engineer. He rented a small office in London at 57 Gracechurch Street, one of the thoroughfares

*William Preece records his voice on the Phonograph built with Henry's help for a lecture given to the Royal Institution on February 1st, 1878 - the first demonstration of sound recording in Britain. (From **The London Weekly Graphic**, March 16th, 1878)*

that converge on the Monument to the Great Fire of London. His recent meetings with Edison gave him an ideal opportunity to publicize his business and gain some valuable personal prestige - the kind of opportunity that every entrepreneur needs when launching a new venture.

By now, news that a 'talking machine' had been invented in America had filtered across the Atlantic, the January 4th issue of *The English Mechanic* having published a letter on the subject from Edison's assistant, Charles Batchelor. More details were eagerly awaited and one of the first things that Henry did when he arrived in London was to contact Perry F. Nursey, chief reporter on *The Times*, who subsequently devoted thirty column inches of his January 17th issue to an article on the Phonograph that began:

> Not many weeks have passed since we were startled by the announcement that we could converse audibly with each other, although hundreds of miles apart, by means of so many miles of wire with a little electro magnet at each end, yet we are on the point of realizing some of the many advantages promised by the telephone. Another wonder is now promised us - an invention, purely mechanical in nature, by means of which words spoken by the human voice can be, so to speak, stored up and reproduced at will over and over again, hundreds, it may be thousands, of times. What will be thought of a piece of mechanism by means of which a message of any length can be spoken on to a plate of metal, that plate sent by post to any part of the world and the message absolutely re-spoken in the very voice of the

sender purely by mechanical agency? What, too, shall be said of a mere machine by means of which the old familiar voice of one who is no longer with us on earth can be heard speaking to us in the very tones and measure to which our ears were once accustomed?

Nursey concluded his very full account of the way the Phonograph worked with these words:

Numerous applications suggest themselves but ... it is difficult to say with precision how they would work out in practice. In cases of depositions, it might be of the highest importance to have oral evidence mechanically reproduced in a court of justice. Authors, too, may be saved the trouble of writing their compositions. We should add that we are indebted for our information to Mr Henry Edmunds ... who has lately returned from a tour of scientific inspection in the United States and is interesting himself in Mr Edison's inventions.

Henry was soon able to make even greater progress in his efforts to promote the Phonograph. On February 1st, William Preece was due to deliver a lecture to the Royal Institution of Great Britain, founded in London in 1799 for the 'promotion, diffusion and extension of science and useful knowledge.' Its laboratory, library and museum in Albemarle Street were already world-famous, and its weekly evening lectures were well supported. Preece had decided to talk about the telephone but after Henry had told him about Edison's recording machine he decided to lecture on this also and asked Henry to help Augustus Stroh, his assistant, make a Phonograph. Henry quickly sketched out a set of drawings and by working day and night Stroh was able to complete, in time for Preece's talk, the first Phonograph to be built in Britain. Years later, Henry described the machine as having 'a clock-driven revolving cylinder'; if that was the case, it would have been more advanced than Edison's prototype, which was hand operated. However, a contemporary sketch shows Preece cranking a handle to turn his machine's cylinder; the clockwork version Henry remembered would have been another Phonograph that Stroh made, for Preece's second lecture on sound recording, given to the Society of Telegraph Engineers on February 27th. *The London Weekly Graphic* described what happened at his first lecture:

> After remarking on the difficulty of knowing what to say under the circumstances, and that he should repeat something he had learnt years ago, Mr Preece spoke into the Phonograph 'Hey, diddle, diddle, the cat and the fiddle,' very distinctly, and after waiting a minute or so the instrument was caused to repeat what he had said. The words were distinctly heard but the voice was very faint and an unearthly caricature. Professor Tyndall then made his way to the table and gave the phonograph a well-known quotation from the pen of Mr Tennyson, who was present, 'Come into the garden, Maud,' which was afterwards echoed to the satisfaction of the audience.

The occasion could not conclude without a contribution from the person who had brought details of the Phonograph to England, and enabled one to be built there before the first models arrived from America. Although photographs of Henry

EDISON'S ELECTRICAL PEN AND DUPLICATING PRESS.

CHAS. BATCHELOR: General Agent for Foreign Countries.
P.O. Box 3207.

Menlo Park N.J.
Feby 12th 1878

Henry Edmunds Esq.

Dear Sir

Unfortunately you addressed your letter to N.Y. Office and the stupid boy in the office only handed them to me today. A few days after you left I made arrangements with Mr Theodore Puskas for the telephone & phonograph on the continent, the paying for the patent. His arrangement did not include England, However he arrived in England some six days ago and Telegraphed if he can sell phonograph patent, and I telegraphed yes if price is satisfactory to me, that was two days ago & I have heard nothing since, but may do so at any moment. He is stopping at the Langham Hotel and has got Telephone and Phonograph. I have given Mr Preece a phonograph which left on City of ... I will send you one immediately it is done, I am very that I could not have done something sooner as you have been so kind. However I will put you

Edison's letter to Henry Edmunds, February 12th 1878.

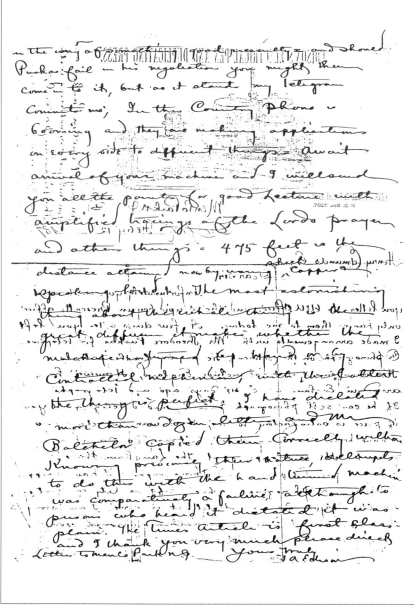

Edison's letter to Henry Edmunds. (continued)

portray him as a rather solemn man, he enjoyed light music and poetry. Bending towards the Phonograph's mouthpiece, he sang:

> Ho! Ho! Ho!
> He'll chuckle and crow.
> What? Marry old Margery?
> No! No! No!

There were shrieks of delight when the song was played back. Henry left his own account of that memorable evening:

> William Preece was enthusiastically cheered and applauded; although no one there understood at that time what would be the future developments of the epoch-making inventions that had been described to them ... today we can barely realize what the world was like without telephones and gramophones. It is one of my greatest pleasures to recall that I was there ... when speech recording and speech transmission were first publicly introduced to the English people.

As a result of making possible the first demonstration of sound recording in Britain, Henry became a minor celebrity in London's scientific community. On February 27th, he joined the Society of Telegraph Engineers (forerunner of today's Institution of Electrical Engineers), on the day that Preece delivered his lecture on sound recording to the society. Henry was now working on three inventions of his own - an 'improved telephone transmitter', an instrument for transmitting sound signals underwater, and a device for recovering tin and iron from tinplate waste - but his main concerns in the early months of 1878 were to promote

William Wallace's arc lighting system and to become involved in the commercial exploitation of Edison's inventions, especially the Phonograph.

Having helped August Stroh build a replica, Henry was anxious to obtain an original Phonograph. He wrote several letters to Edison, urging him to despatch one at once. In the Edison archives at West Orange, New Jersey, there is a copy of one of Edison's replies, dated February 12th and written on the letterhead of Edison's Electrical Pen and Duplicating Press, the first duplicating process to employ a wax stencil. In his letter to Henry, hurriedly written and lapsing occasionally into 'telegramese,' Edison said:

> A few days after you left I made arrangements with Mr Theodore Puskas for Telephone and Phonograph on the Continent, he paying for the patents. His arrangements did not include England. However he arrived in England some six days ago and Telegraphs if he can sell Phonograph patent, and I telegraphed 'yes' if price is satisfactory to me; that was two days ago. I have heard nothing since, but may do so at any moment. He is stopping at the Langham Hotel and has pair Telephones and 2 Phonographs - I have shipped Mr Preece a Phonograph which left on *City of Montreal*. I will send you one immediately it is done; I am sorry that I could not have done something through you as you have been so kind. However I will put you in the way of something good presently - and should Puskas fail in his negotiations you might then come in to it, but as it stands my telegram commits me.

An autographed photograph of Thomas Edison, given to Henry Edmunds in 1923.

In this country phone is booming and they are making applications on every side to different things. Await arrival of your machine and I will send you all the points for good lecture, with amplified tracings of the Lord's Prayer and other things. 475 feet is the distance attained now by using sheet copper and speaking loud. The astonishing thing about the whole thing is the great difference it makes whether the machine is turned by hand or by controlled mechanism, with the latter the thing is perfect. I have dictated more than a dozen letters and Mr Batchelor copied them perfectly without knowing previously their nature. Attempts to do this with the hand turned machine was [sic] comparatively a failure; although to persons who heard it dictated it was plain. *The Times* article is first class and I thank you very much.

PS. You might call on Puskas and you may do something with the Russian patent. Puskas is a good man and a gentleman.

Theodore Puskas, Edison's foreign patent lawyer, had made too much progress for Henry to have any chance of obtaining a licence to exploit the Phonograph patents in Britain - the London Stereoscopic Company was the successful applicant - but Henry was still keen to do what he could, and on February 26th he wrote to Edison:

I am sorry you cannot put the Phonograph into my hands commercially but I am pleased you will let me lecture and exhibit scientifically. I have promised to read a paper before the Society of Arts. I am

only waiting your notes, diagrams and Phonograph, which I hope you will send off per first
steamer, or else write me definitely when they will
be here, as the Soc. do not wish to postpone the
paper any longer than can be helped. I have
written a good deal of a paper already, and shall
now wait till I hear from you. I am glad you were
pleased with the article in *The Times*. It caused
quite a sensation here in England. Please keep me
posted up as to all improvements and new inventions. I shall be pleased to do all I can for you in
introducing them here.

The day after Henry wrote this letter, William Preece
delivered his lecture to the Society of Telegraph Engineers.
He demonstrated three machines. One of these was another
copy of Edison's original Phonograph, made by W. Pidgeon.
The second was an improved model, sent over by Edison,
which recorded and played-back through a single diaphragm
and was equipped with a heavy flywheel to control the
cylinder's rate of rotation. The third machine, also a 'single
diaphragm' model, was the clockwork version constructed
by Augustus Stroh. Its motor was driven by a falling weight
and controlled by a speed governor.

After receiving Henry's letter of February 26th, Edison
replied cordially on March 12th:

> Friend Edmunds! ... One of my assistants leaves
> for England on the 16th and carries with him 2
> small Phonographs. I will instruct him to go with
> you and assist you when you deliver your lecture
> ... since you left I have the articulation perfect,
> reproducing whispers.

Henry was annoyed that Edison had still not despatched the Phonograph promised four weeks earlier. On April 2nd he wrote again to Edison:

> Your assistant, Mr Adams ... dined with me yesterday. I was much surprised to find you had not sent me a Phonograph as promised in yours of February 12th. As I explained [to] Adams, it puts me in a very awkward position with the public scientific men here, to whom I showed your letters. However, if you would kindly send me one per first mail it will make it all right. Also I should be pleased if you will kindly put something else in my way as soon as you have something good, for I am sure I can introduce here for you in the best manner, both among scientific and business men ... Please write me soon and let me have Phono at once.

Clearly, Adams - probably James Adams, one of Edison's most skilled craftsmen, but a chronic alcoholic - had turned up empty-handed. No other letters from Henry to Edison have survived to tell us exactly how the saga of the long-awaited Phonograph ended but Henry did eventually obtain it. Colonel George Gouraud became Edison's agent in Britain; Henry gradually lost touch with Edison but 10 years later he found himself in the curious position of working closely with some of his American friend's fiercest competitors in the race to build an improved 'talking machine.'

PART TWO
'Her Majesty spoke a few words'

In October 1878, Edison abandoned further work on sound recording so that he could devote all his time to developing a cheap and efficient electric lamp. Other inventors, however, saw just as bright a future for the 'talking machine'. Among those that became interested in the subject was Alexander Graham Bell, who as professor of vocal physiology at Boston University had been closely concerned with the plight of deaf-mutes. His studies involved him in experiments in speech therapy and acoustics that led to the invention of the first telephone capable of sustained articulate speech. Bell's telephone call to his assistant on March 10th, 1876 - "Come here, Watson, I want you" - was as important a moment in technological history as Edison's recital of the words "Mary had a little lamb" on his tinfoil Phonograph on December 6th, 1877. In 1880, Bell received the $10,000 Volta Prize from the French government for his invention, He used the money to set up the Volta Laboratory in Washington, DC to carry out further research into sound reproduction and acoustics. In 1881, he decided that his next project would be to improve Edison's Phonograph. He was assisted by his cousin, Chichester A. Bell, a chemical engineer and Charles Sumner Tainter, a scientist and instrument maker. Together they carried out a complete review of the way in which the Phonograph worked. Edison's crude needle and diaphragm, his fiddly, fragile foil and his jerky, hand-cranked cylinder would forever have confined the instrument to the playroom but the Bell cousins and Tainter had better ideas. In trying to find a new way of recording and reproducing sound they experimented with jets of air, water and even (one hundred years before the invention of laser-activated compact discs) beams of light. None of these methods was satisfactory and eventually they developed a 'floating' reproducing stylus which followed the grooves in the record more accurately than Edison's rigid needle.

In searching for a better recording medium than tinfoil, Bell and his team chose a wax compound. At one stage they stepped ahead of their time and considered recording on wax discs, even specifying them in their first patent application for their improved Phonograph, but when the machine finally appeared its records were cylindrical in shape and made of wax-coated cardboard. The cylinders were rotated at a more or less constant speed by a foot-operated treadle, similar to those fitted to the sewing machines of the day. The recording stylus cut a spiral groove in the wax, and as it did so the vibrations created by the sound waves engraved a pattern of perpendicular vibrations or 'hills and dales' in the base of the groove. Sound reproduction was clearer than that of Edison's Phonograph, but quieter, so the recordings had to be listened to through a kind of stethoscope.

The new machine was called the Bell-Tainter Graphophone and patented in May 1886, but before its inventors announced it to the public they sent a prototype to Edison, hoping that he would make further improvements and become their partner in a joint venture to launch the machine commercially. They acknowledged that Edison was the true inventor of the 'talking machine'; said that they wanted to cooperate, not compete, with him; and offered to turn all their work over to him, bear all the costs of experimental work, and invest capital in the venture, in return for a fifty per cent interest in the enterprise.

Edison was furious and accused the Bell cousins and Tainter of stealing his invention. Examining the prototype they had left with him, he declared astonishment that it had been granted a patent, since in his eyes it contained nothing new except the improved stylus. The patent had, in fact, been applied for on June 27th, 1885, so Edison and his legal staff had had plenty of warning of its imminent introduction. After rejecting Bell's offer of a joint venture, Edison at last set to work to make his own improvements to the Phonograph. From now on he gave the impression that he had always intended to resume work on sound recording after he had developed the incandescent electric lamp. Whether or not that was so, during the next two years he made up for lost time and on June 16th, 1888, he unveiled the prototype of his "Perfected Phonograph." A famous photograph taken at the time shows the dishevelled, fatigued inventor slumped behind the prototype after he and his assistants had worked for five days and nights to get it to work satisfactorily. Ostensibly the Graphophone and the latest Phonograph were identical, although there were important differences in their details. Edison's cylinders were made of solid wax, were thicker than those of the Graphophone, and could be shaved smooth to erase previous recordings allowing new ones to be made. Because the groove was only one-thousandth of an inch deep the cylinders could be re-used many times; Graphophone cylinders could be recorded upon only once. The Phonograph recorded by forming impressions or indentations in the cylinder's groove, whereas the Graphophone actually cut material from the groove. And to drive the cylinder when recordings were made and played back, the Phonograph had an electric motor.

In 1887, while Edison was struggling to regain his lead in the field of sound recording, the Bells and Tainter sold their interest in the Graphophone to the American Graphophone Company, which had its headquarters in Washington, DC and regarded the government departments there as a ready-made market for dictating machines; the Graphophone seemed ideal for this purpose.

It was at this time, when an open conflict between Edison and his rivals seemed inevitable, that Henry Edmunds made another of his periodic visits to the USA, where he now had several business associates. In 1886 he had become a partner of Walter Twiss Glover, who owned an electric cable factory in Manchester. One purpose of Henry's trip to America in 1887 was to see if there were any new ideas that he and Glover could introduce into Britain. We do not know if Henry was specifically interested in the imminent renaissance of the "talking machine", but he arrived there at an important stage in the development of the Graphophone. The Bell cousins and Tainter had just, or would soon, sell their interest in the machine to the American Graphophone Company but its foreign rights had not yet been disposed of. Somewhat brazenly, the company asked Colonel George Gouraud, Edison's British agent, if he would like to head a British agency for the Graphophone, but when Gouraud sent a cablegram to Edison from London asking for his approval he was told: "Have nothing to do with them. They are [a] bunch [of] pirates." Edison's response was despatched on August 1st, 1887. Soon after this date, Henry Edmunds visited Washington, DC, where he was introduced to Tainter by Philip Mauro, a patent agent (and soon to become Bell-Tainter's attorney). Some control over the Graphophone's promotion was evidently still retained by Tainter and the Volta Laboratory, and Tainter was able to appoint Henry as

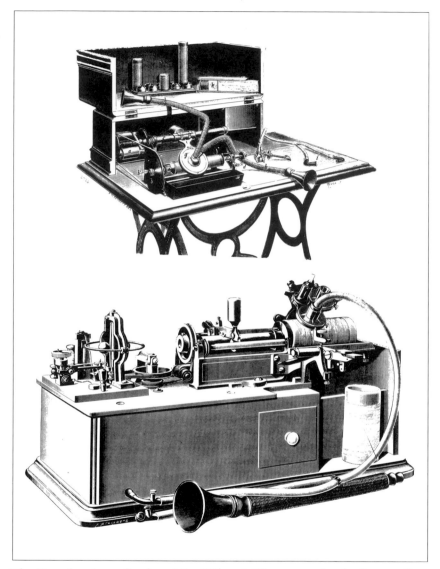

The Graphophone (top) and the Edison's Phonograph, rival recording machines demonstrated to the British Association's conference at Bath in 1888. The small box among the cylinders above the Graphophone bears Henry Edmunds' name and address. (From Engineering, September 14th, 1888)

his European representative.

It was not until the summer of 1888 that the Graphophone and Edison's new Phonograph were shown to the American public. Meanwhile, Jesse H. Lippincott, a millionaire manufacturer from Pittsburgh, had invested $200,000 in the American Graphophone Company and become its sole licensee, with exclusive rights to promote the machine in the USA. Lippincott had also bought the patent rights to Edison's Phonograph for $500,000 and formed the North American Phonograph Company to sell the machine. The Phonograph rapidly underwent three stages of improvement in 1887 and 1888, culminating in the Perfected Phonograph, embodying a battery-powered electric motor to turn the cylinder and a governor and flywheel to regulate the cylinder's speed. The Graphophone's lack of an electric motor was not quite such a disadvantage as may appear, since the primitive battery that drove Edison's machine had a life of only fifteen hours.

This, then, was the "state of the art" when the Graphophone was introduced into Britain. In July 1888 Henry made another visit to America; on August 3rd *The Electrician* announced:

> We hear that Mr Henry Edmunds ... is bringing some Graphophones back from the States and will probably read a paper on the Graphophone before the British Association.

Formed in 1831, the British Association for the Advancement of Science has, as one of its objectives, the dissemination of popular knowledge of science. It holds its annual conferences in various British Commonwealth countries and British provincial cities, the venue in 1888 being Bath, the most celebrated of Britain's spa cities. Before the conference opened, Henry demonstrated the Graphophone at his London office, which was now at 10 Hatton Gardens, in some ways repeating his triumph of 1878, when he brought news of Edison's tinfoil Phonograph to England. A reporter from *The Electrician* went along to Henry's office to find out about the new instrument:

> On the day of our visit a phonogram had just been received from Mr Chichester A. Bell ... his voice is well known to us and was instantly recognized as soon as the machine was set in motion. Owing to rough treatment in the post the cylinder had been quite bent out of shape and we were agreeably surprised to find that in spite of this, only one or two words out of a long letter were slightly indistinct ... The machine is driven by a treadle... the work required to drive it is much less than for a sewing machine and a small electric motor may of course be used if desired. The inventors, however, are of the opinion that it is better dispensed with so long as primary batteries have to be used as the source of energy and we have no doubt that such of our readers as have used primary batteries to drive electro motors will agree with us.

The reporter went on to describe how the rotation of the cylinder and the movement of the recording or reproducing stylus along the wax surface (for pauses in dictation or transcription) could be halted by pressing a small lever: 'a very much simpler arrangement than the one used for the same purpose in Edison's new phonograph'. Another great advantage was that, once properly adjusted by the makers, the Graphophone needed no further attention, whereas Edison's machine had to be adjusted every time a cylinder was put on and therefore could only be used satisfactorily by an expert.

The British public had its first opportunity to compare the two latest talking machines on September 6th, 1888, at the Masonic Hall, Bath, where papers on the Graphophone and the latest Phonograph were presented by Henry Edmunds and Colonel Gouraud respectively. Henry began his presentation by reviewing the history of man's first attempts to record and transmit sound. He then spoke of his visit to Edison's laboratory at the time of the invention of the Phonograph, his efforts to promote the machine in Britain in 1878, and Edison's subsequent abandonment of the Phonograph until provoked into resuming his work by news of the progress that had been made at the Volta Laboratory. In a statement that would not have been well received at West Orange, New Jersey, where Edison had recently relocated his laboratory, Henry said.

> All praise accorded to Mr Edison and his agents for the 'improved Phonograph' is fairly due to Mr Charles Sumner Tainter and his associates.

He went on to describe the Graphophone and its uses in more detail:

> The Graphophone as shown here is propelled mechanically. The whole has been designed to attain the best results with the fewest parts and absence of skilled attention. There is no electricity. An ordinary treadle ... rotates a speed governor. This by a leather belt communicates a con-

stant speed to the rotating wax cylinder. A diaphragm of mica carrying a steel graver, called the recorder, is mounted in a metal holder which by means of a revolving screw traverses the wax cylinder, cutting a fine thread 100 to the inch. A mouthpiece attached to a flexible tube carries the sound vibrations to the diaphragm which causes the graver or style to cut into the wax a series of depressions more or less frequent, and varying in depth according to the sounds producing the vibrations. These undulations, while so slight as to be barely perceptible, can, nevertheless, produce in the diaphragm of the reproducer similar vibrations to the original sounds and give back, not once, but indefinitely, the words or sounds which were first recorded ... Great economy has been found in the use of a cardboard cylinder coated with wax instead of solid wax cylinders. They are more easily handled, less liable to fracture, and much lighter for postage, besides being cheaper than notepaper, when the saving of time in writing is considered. The very simplicity of the instrument startles us ... its introduction into every-day life marks a new era. Truly the unlimited reproduction of the human voice in speech and song is a most wonderful achievement. When we consider its marvellous adaptability to modern life, there seems to be no limit to its powers. A child may work it and communicate to those who love it, its childish prattle; or preserving the small cylinder refer in after life to how it spoke. Business men may carry on negotiations, recording each word spoken, preventing misunderstandings as to what was said ... the stenographer may read his notes to it, leaving it to dictate to others to write them out.

Henry also suggested how a Graphophone could be attached to a telephone, to allow "fleeting words to be recorded for future reference." He had in fact, on the day before his lecture, filed a patent application for such a device. At about this time, he and Walter Glover formally set up their Graphophone agency; the Glover papers in the North West Museum of Science and Industry in Manchester contain an entry dated September 1888 which reads:

Started on Graphophone account. Took out patents in colonies. Sold interest to Sydney Morse account for £1,000. Paid Volta Graphophone Co. Washington £4,086.

While at Bath, Henry attended a lecture on atomic theory by the British Association's President, Sir Frederick Bramwell, and listened to Lord Kelvin, Professor Silvanus Thompson, William Preece and Sir Oliver Lodge discuss such subjects as 'the true nature of electricity'. He also met John Glaisher, the pioneer balloonist and founder of the Royal Meteorological Society. Glaisher showed a keen interest in sound recording and may have been among the many members of the association who recorded their voices on Henry's Graphophone. Three months after addressing the BA, Henry became a member of the Royal Society of Arts, a learned society founded in London in 1754 to promote the practical arts and sciences. Its pioneering work had already included the Great Exhibition of 1851 (the world's first international exhibition)

Sydney Morse (circled) – the man who recorded Queen Victoria, photographed whilst a member of the England rugby union team that played Scotland in Glasgow in 1873.

and the advent of a practical method of recording and reproducing sound was of considerable interest to its members. On the day he was elected a member, Henry delivered a lecture on the Graphophone to the society and commented upon the reaction the instrument had received since he first showed it at Bath:

> I have been much interested to note the enormous diversity of uses that have been suggested. Physicians ask for it in order that when returning home late at night they, without any fatigue, may simply speak into the machine as to the condition of the patient visited and suggest the necessary treatment. It is also suggested that residents in Bournemouth or Nice need not come to London to consult their medical men but can send samples of their cough by Graphophone, thus indicating the improvement or condition of their lungs. Blind people may also through the medium of their ears avail themselves of avenues of instruction and amusement to which their eyes have been so long closed. The small tradesman who cannot afford to have his own bookkeeper, and has not time during the press of business to put down the verbal orders he receives, or the sales he is making, can incidentally speak to this instrument, recording each transaction, and leisurely take off the words thus spoken later in the day, entering them into book form. Connected to the telephone the other day, I was enabled to record the words spoken and to recall afterwards that which I had forgotten in the hurry of the moment, viz. whether I had made

an appointment to meet a friend at London Bridge
at six minutes past five or five minutes past six.

Henry left five Graphophones in the RSA's library for a few
days, so that members could examine them at their leisure.

In the aftermath of the British debut of the Graphophone
and the improved Phonograph, Henry Edmunds and Colonel
Gouraud achieved a great deal of publicity for their machines. Gouraud put the Phonograph on display at the
Crystal Palace and persuaded William Gladstone, Lord
Tennyson and Robert Browning to record their voices; but it
was Henry who had the greatest success in recording the
voices of the famous, even though at the time he was not
allowed to publicize the fact. Here, from his *Reminiscences*,
is his own account of what happened:

> My offices in Hatton Garden were thronged with
> persons of all grades of society, all astonished
> with the new Gramophone [sic]. Its fame even
> reached the ears of Royalty and the aged Queen
> Victoria expressed a desire to have a demonstra-
> tion at Balmoral Castle. I could not go myself but
> my friend and solicitor, Mr Sydney Morse, took an
> instrument to Scotland and had the honour of
> showing it to the delightful old lady. Abandoning
> the usual Royal reserve, Her Majesty expressed
> her unqualified delight; so much so that Mr Morse
> was emboldened to request the Queen to speak a
> few words into the Gramophone. As is well known,
> Queen Victoria strongly objected to autograph
> hunters and all that sort of folk; and now she was
> asked to give, not merely a specimen of the Royal
> signature, but a record of a Royal voice! However,

> her admiration of the new invention overcame her
> scruples; and Mr Morse exhibited to me a small
> black cylinder with a few spiral lines traced upon
> it, containing the record of the voice and speech of
> the celebrated Queen. He declared that it was his
> most cherished possession; and would pass it to
> his children as his chiefest treasure.

The archives of recorded sound contain recordings of many voices of members of the British Royal family, including Queen Victoria's cousin, the Duke of Cambridge, who in 1888 recorded a message to Thomas Edison on a Phonograph cylinder. The earliest surviving documented recording of a reigning monarch is one of King George V, made in the 1920s. The most obvious omission from the archives is a recording of the voice of Queen Victoria. On August 8th, 1898 (some ten years after Henry received his 'Royal Command') she did record a message on a cylinder for Emperor Menelik of Abyssinia but instructed that it should be destroyed after it had been played to him. When the cylinder was delivered to the Emperor he stood to attention and welcomed it with an artillery salute; a few days later, the cylinder was returned to the Queen's agent in Abyssinia, Captain Harrington, and was immediately broken into pieces, as promised*. Menelik had been highly honoured; in 1897 the Queen had been asked by the Edison Bell Phonograph Corporation to make a recording to commemorate her Diamond Jubilee, but the company was told that she had previously declined all similar invitations and would not make an exception in this case. Further invitations in 1899 and 1900 were also re-

*The Letters of Queen Victoria. Third Series, Vol. III. G.E. Buckle (Ed). John Murray, 1932.

fused. Henry Edmunds's revelation, in the early 1920s, that Queen Victoria had been persuaded to record her voice in 1888, the year after her Golden Jubilee, did not encourage anyone to try and find the 'small black cylinder' with its 'few spiral traces,' or discover more about the occasion on which the recording was made, but while researching the Queen's life for her book *Victoria R.I.* the Countess of Longford found out about it and wrote:

> What the Queen called 'treats', including profes-
> sional theatricals, became plentiful after the Ju-
> bilee ... a gramophone [sic] was brought to Bal-
> moral by Mr Morse and after the household had
> recorded whistles and German jokes Her Majesty
> spoke a few words. Mr Morse was warned not to
> tour the country playing them.*

Queen Victoria's request to hear the Graphophone was characteristic of the interest she took in the new inventions that were being introduced during her reign. In January 1878 Britain's first private telephone line was installed at Osborne House, her home on the Isle of Wight. Her telephone was connected to a telegraph line from the mainland so that she could listen to a spoken message and the sound of a bugler playing the Retreat in Southampton, and an organ playing in London.

Why Henry Edmunds declined the Royal invitation to demonstrate the Graphophone is not known. The Queen was at Balmoral from August 28th until November 15th, 1888; if Henry had an important previous appointment between the time he gave his lecture to the British Association and the

*Weidenfeld and Nicolson, 1964.

time Queen Victoria left Balmoral, he left no account of it. He may, of course, have arranged to make another trip to America in that period. Whatever the reason, Sydney Morse was an ideal deputy. As we know from the Glover papers, he had purchased an interest in Henry Edmunds and Walter Glover's Graphophone agency in September 1888. He was at this time thirty-four years old and embarking on a distinguished legal career. He represented various electric lighting companies in London, and became associated with the promotion of many tramways and light railways. But what were more important than his business activities, so far as his visit to Balmoral was concerned, were his connections with the Royal family. His wife Juliet Mary and his mother-in-law Isabella Tylor are believed to have been ladies-in-waiting in the Royal household at some time, possibly to Queen Victoria's fourth daughter, Princess Louise, who in 1871 married the Marquis of Lorne, the future 9th Duke of Argyll. Neither Mrs Morse or Mrs Tylor are mentioned in the Royal Archives' list of the Princess's ladies-in-waiting - the list is incomplete - but Mrs Tylor was a friend of Madame Rollande, who was French governess to Queen Victoria's children from 1847 until 1859.

The Royal Archives contain a number of letters from Madame Rollande to Mrs Tylor and her husband Albert. One of them refers to a present of doves that Princess Alice, Queen Victoria's second daughter, sent to Juliet Mary and her brother Edward, so it seems that the Royal family and the Tylor family were on friendly terms when their children were young. The friendship continued after Juliet married Sydney Morse, and in the archives there is also a significant letter to Princess Louise from Fraulein Ottilie Bauer, who had been

German governess to Queen Victoria's children and became her Letrice when the children grew up. In early 1907 Juliet and Sydney Morse dined with Princess Louise. Soon afterwards, Juliet wrote to Fraulein Bauer to tell her about the occasion, and on March 15th Fraulein Bauer wrote to Princess Louise, saying:

> Mrs Morse wrote to me after she and her husband had dined with you, but said that unfortunately your wish to hear the voice of the dear Queen had been a disappointment. After so many years this is not to be wondered at, especially as great improvements have no doubt been made to the instrument since then. I remember very well that visit of Mr Morse to Balmoral, after he had received the Queen's permission on our journey there to bring the Phonograph.*

Fraulein Bauer should, of course, have called the instrument a Graphophone but by 1907 all recording machines were becoming known as Phonographs or Gramophones, their future generic names. Fraulein Bauer appears to have been under the impression that Sydney Morse had asked the Queen whether he could take the Graphophone to Balmoral. If so, Henry Edmunds's account of the sequence of events that led up to the Royal recording is incorrect in detail, though not in substance.

The one first-hand account of the occasion that everyone would like to read is, of course, one by Queen Victoria herself. It is highly like that she wrote about Sydney Morse's visit to

*Published by gracious permission of Her Majesty the Queen. RA Add.A17/1043.

Balmoral, and the amusement she derived from the Graphophone, in her famous *Journal*, but as is well known this was transcribed after her death by her youngest daughter, Princess Beatrice, who then destroyed the original. When making her transcription the Princess omitted various passages; perhaps one of them was an account of Sydney's visit? The Queen's Private Secretary, Sir Henry Ponsonby, would have known about the visit, but neither his published letters* nor others in the possession of his grandson, the 3rd Baron Ponsonby of Shulbrede, mention it. Twenty years after researching the life of Queen Victoria, Lady Longford told this author that as far as she could remember, she obtained details of Sydney's visit from the Queen's *Journal*, but that has proved not to be the case. Her correspondence with Sir Robin Mackworth-Young, Royal Librarian at Windsor Castle at the time she was writing her book, does not give any clues about her source.

Although it would be fascinating to discover more details about Queen Victoria's Royal recording, finding the actual cylinder was of far greater importance. Although Henry Edmunds's efforts to launch the Graphophone in Britain generated so much excitement and publicity, he soon lost what proved to be his last chance to gain any lasting benefit from becoming a 'talking machine' pioneer. What has become of the apparatus that he demonstrated during those exciting years? Where are his tinfoil Phonograph, the Graphophone he demonstrated to the British Association,

*Henry Ponsonby, Queen Victoria's Private Secretary; His Life and Letters. Arthur Ponsonby, 1st Baron Ponsonby of Shulbrede. Macmillan & Co., 1942.

and the cylinders on which he made so many recordings? And most important of all, where was the cylinder on which Queen Victoria recorded her voice?

PART THREE
'Greetings, Britons and everybody'

One hundred or more years after Henry Edmunds introduced the Phonograph and Graphophone into Britain, the chances of finding any of his sound recording apparatus were remote, but I decided to make the effort. The obvious first source of enquiry was the Principal Probate Registry at Somerset House, London, where I inspected Henry's Will, but this contained no references to recording machines or cylinders. This did not prove beyond doubt that no equipment of this kind existed among Henry's effects when he died, so enquiries had to made among his descendants. His children Dorothy, Claud and Howard all died long before the research for this book was begun; Claud and Howard both married but only Claud had any children - three daughters, Cicely Edmunds, Dorothy Tornow and Muriel Pritchard. In old age, Henry experienced serious financial difficulties and had to auction most of his property. He died at Hove, Sussex, on November 18th, 1927. His wife Ellen returned to her home town of Providence, Rhode Island, where she died on May 21st, 1928. When I began my project, the few possessions of Henry and Ellen that still remained in their family belonged to Cicely Edmunds or Dr Michael Pritchard, Michael being the oldest of Henry's great-grandchildren. Neither Cicely nor Michael knew whether Henry's recording machines or any of the recordings made on them had survived.

My enquiries outside the family were at first concerned with finding Henry's Phonograph. If he had given this to a museum or an institution the most obvious beneficiarieswould have been the Science Museum, South Kensington, London, or the Royal Institution of Great Britain, where with Henry's help, the first demonstration of sound recording in England had been made in 1878. The

Royal Institution does own an Edison Phonograph, but this is a wax cylinder player, whereas Henry's machine was a tinfoil player. The Science Museum's inventory of early talking machines was then checked, without success.

Quite by coincidence, my hopes that the Phonograph had survived were raised only a few days after they had been dashed at the Royal Institution and the Science Museum. As part of my general efforts to contact anyone who remembered Henry Edmunds, I broadcast on BBC Radio Brighton's "Good Morning" programme and managed to get stories about my project published in various local newspapers. Among those who responded were Leonard and Violet Simmonds, who had been servants to Henry and Ellen when they had lived at Moulscoombe Place, Brighton, in the 1920s. Leonard remembered that Henry had sold a Phonograph to Mr Hay, a gramophone and cycle dealer in Brighton, before the contents of Moulscoombe were auctioned on March 25th and 26th, 1927.

Would it be possible, more than fifty years later, to trace the machine? While following up leads in Brighton, I made further enquiries at the Science Museum, in case the Phonograph had at any time been offered to its collection, or displayed temporarily; these enquiries revealed that a Mr John Hay had loaned a tinfoil phonograph for a special exhibition held in 1977 to commemorate the invention's centenary. It seemed safe to assume that this machine and the one sold to Mr Hay in 1927 were one and the same, and this was confirmed when I contacted John Hay, the managing director of Walport Limited, suppliers of entertainment equipment to shipping companies and a director of Henry Stave and Co., classical record dealers. John told me that he was co-owner of the Phonograph with his brother Peter, and that their father, John, was the man who had bought the machine from Henry. Although no longer in working order it is virtually intact and capable of being restored. On its base there are two inscriptions: "Manufactured by S. Bergman & Co., No 104 Wooster, NY" and "Experimental apparatus for illustrating the principle of Edison's speaking Phonograph, Patented February 19, 1878, No 205". In a drawer in the base there are some tools, a few original sheets of tinfoil and an instruction manual. This is signed "H. Edmunds" and has the imprint of a stamp bearing the name of the Edison Speaking Phonograph Company and its treasurer, E. H. Johnson. A diagram on page three of the manual confirms that the machine is an "exhibition instrument" made for public performances at entertainment halls and amusement centres.

Unfortunately the sheets of tinfoil are blank; how fascinating it would have been if Henry had left some recordings of his own voice and the voices of those to whom he demonstrated the machine, He did, however, hand down some interesting documents, including an unsigned letter in his own handwriting, and a typed transcription of it, which he signed. Both read as follows:-

> The Phonograph which you have purchased from me is of considerable historical interest. I was in America in 1877 and first met Mr Edison at the house of a friend with whom I was staying in August. Later, in December I called to see Mr Edison at Menloe [sic], New Jersey, at his laboratory. I found him experimenting with several of his assistants in connection with an apparatus con-

Henry Edmunds' Edison Phonograph

John Hay, with Henry's Edison Phonograph.

sisting of a cylinder on which a spiral groove had been cut, which was covered with tinfoil. Mr Edison had just spoken into a mouthpiece holding a tin diaphragm with a metal point which through vibrations produced a series of impressions on the tinfoil. When this was afterwards revolved, it spoke the words "Mary had a little lamb". Later in 1879, Mr Edison gave me the phonograph you have purchased - the first one to come to Europe* - I brought it myself in 1879.

Yours faithfully

Henry Edmunds

MIEE, M Inst C.E".

The letter is undated but must have been written to Mr Hay after January 16th 1927, the day when Henry wrote the letter quoted in Part One, in which he described his visit to Menlo Park and said, "I still have an original photograph sent me the year after, which I treasure greatly.

Also among the documents is a copy of a letter from H. G. Lyons, Director of the Science Museum, dated July 11th, 1930 asking John Hay Snr. to donate the machine to the Science Museum. In September 1930, a press agency, the Christian Science Monitor Bureau, reported that an appeal by the Institute of Physics in London for "old apparatus used by inventors in making their discoveries" had brought to light

---

*Henry was mistaken. Other tinfoil Phonographs had been sent to Europe in 1878. Henry's instrument, Phonograph No. 205, was sold to Thomas Edison for $90 in July 1879, presumably by the Edison Speaking Phonograph Co., which had the sole rights to exploit, manufacture and sell Edison's apparatus. Henry returned to the USA in 1879 and met Edison for the third time, and this was when he at last obtained the Phonograph he had been so anxious to acquire. Edison, it seems, had to buy one for Henry!

a replica of Edison's first Phonograph and that its owners, a firm of gramophone dealers in Brighton, had lent it to the Science Museum. However, it appears from the other papers in John and Peter Hay's possession that Lyons did not accept their father's offer to lend, rather than donate, the machine to the museum. It was displayed in Brighton Museum for a brief period, and perhaps in Hay's shop in North Street, before being placed in its original case and stored in the shop's attic for nearly fifty years.

It was, for all intents and purposes, forgotten and undisturbed during this time, which perhaps explains why its general condition and livery belie its age. In 1977, John Hay recovered the instrument from the attic in order to put it on show that April and May at an exhibition of "One hundred years of recorded sound" at a new shop opened by Henry Stave in Great Marlborough Street, London. It was last seen by the public at the Science Museum's exhibition in 1977 but seems to have attracted very little attention, probably because it was placed in a rather obscure position.

After the exhibition John Hay stored the instrument at the London office of Walport Limited, where it remained until interest in it was reawakened once again, while I was researching Henry Edmunds' life.

Having located the most important relic of Henry Edmunds' connections with the Phonograph, my next task was to try and find one of his Graphophones or the cylinders made and played on them; preferably Sydney Morse's recording of Queen Victoria! At this stage in the research, the most recent documentary proof of its existence was Fraulein Bauer's letter of March 15th, 1907, to Princess Louise, one of Queen Victoria's daughters. From this it appears that the "Royal"

Dear Sir,

The phonograph which you have purchased from [...] considerable Historic interest.

I was in America in 1877 and first met Mr. [Edison at the] house of a friend with whom I was staying [...] in December I called to see Mr. Edison [at Menlo Park, New Jersey,] at his laboratory. I found him experimenting with some [of] his assistants in connection with an apparatus [consisting of] a cylinder on which a spiral groove had been cut, [which was] covered with tin foil. Mr. Edison had just spoken into a mouth-piece holding a tin diaphragm with a metal point which through the vibrations produced a series of impressions on the tin foil. When this was afterwards revolved, it spoke the words "Mary had a little lamb".

Later in 1879, Mr. Edison gave me the phonograph you have purchased - the first one [to come] to Europe - I brought it myself in 1879.

yours faithfully

Henry Edmunds
M.I.E.E. M.I.M.E.C.E.

Henry Edmunds' letter to John Hay about his Phonograph.

recording cylinder still existed in 1907 and that Sydney and
Juliet Morse took it with them when they went to dine with
Princess Louise, intending to play it so that they could all
hear the Queen's voice again. Queen Victoria died on January 22nd, 1901, and it is possible that the Morses and
Princess Louise dined together on a date very close to the
sixth anniversary of the Queen's death. The attempt to play
the cylinder failed, and the reason for this could have been
that Princess Louise owned a Phonograph, not a Graphophone.
The cylinder was a Graphophone recording and could be
played only on a Graphophone. The Morses had a
Graphophone of course, but this would never have been an
easy object to take to a dinner party!

The search for the cylinder would probably have petered
out after the discovery of Fraulein Bauer's letter, but for a
fortunate coincidence.

While providing me with details of Henry's tinfoil Phonograph, and allowing it to be examined and photographed,
John Hay asked about Henry Edmunds's career during the
early days of sound recording. When I told him about Sydney
Morse and his visit to Balmoral, Mr Hay replied: "My solicitors are Waltons & Morse. I wonder if there is any connection?" There was. Sydney Morse, who in his youth distinguished himself by playing rugby for England for three years
in succession from 1873, qualified as a solicitor in 1878, the
year in which he married Juliet Tylor. He headed his own
practice, Sydney Morse & Co., in London; at one time he had
offices in Queen Street but in 1925 the firm moved to Alder
House, Aldersgate Street. Sydney died on January 27th,
1929, aged seventy-five, leaving a widow and four children:
Francis Alfred Vivian, Mary Enid, Leopold George Esmond

and John Anthony Vere. The first two forenames for L.G.E. Morse were chosen by Princess Louise, who was his godmother, but he was always known as Esmond. After Sydney's death his practice was continued by his partners who, naturally, were retained as the Morse family's solicitors. In 1975 the firm amalgamated with Waltons & Co. and the combined practice moved to Plantation House, Fenchurch Street. Was there a chance that, more than fifty years after Sydney's death, any of his descendants, friends of the family or former employees would know what had become of his recording of Queen Victoria, or of any of the Graphophones that he and Henry Edmunds had demonstrated to the noble and famous?

One phrase in Henry's account of Sydney's visit to Balmoral had special significance: "He declared that [the recording] was his most cherished possession; and would pass it to his children as his chiefest treasure." Perhaps this meant that he had included a specific instruction to this effect in his Will? Unfortunately he had not. He made his Will in June, 1914, bequeathing books, silver plate, prints, china and a considerable collection of pictures and other works of art to his children, but neither his cherished Royal recording, nor any Graphophones, are mentioned. In a codicil dated March 4th, 1916, Sydney directed that, instead of being equally divided among his children, his valuables should be sold at Christie's, "where any member of my family will be able to buy any lot they may specially desire to retain." Sydney added no less than nine codicils to his Will, the last dated September 28th, 1928, but they contain no references to recording apparatus.

The obvious assumption was that, sometime between

1907 and the day on which he made his Will seven years later, Sydney gave the 'Queen Victoria' cylinder to his children (nominating one of them to be its keeper); on the other hand, he could have lost, broken or discarded it during those seven years, but this would have been out of character for someone who was accustomed to preserving valuable objects, and had been a close acquaintance, or even a friend, of Queen Victoria.

Proof that the cylinder had survived after 1907 was eventually obtained in 1980. By now, none of Morse's four children was still living but with the help of Philip English, a senior partner at Waltons & Morse and John Holgate, who had been a junior clerk at Sydney Morse & Co. during the last years of Morse's life, I traced two of Sydney's grandchildren - Mary Barton (a daughter of L.G.E. Morse) and David Morse (son of F.A.V. Morse) - and a great-grandchild, Charles Ainley. Mr Ainley searched through his large collection of family correspondence dating back to the 1880s but could find no references to the cylinder; nor could he recall his mother, a daughter of J.A.V. Morse, ever mentioning it. However, Mrs Barton and David Morse recalled hearing the cylinder. Mrs Barton said:

> I remember seeing cylinders which I was told were records made by my grandfather, and that one of them was the recording of Queen Victoria. Some time during my childhood in the 1920s I heard my grandfather playing the voice of the Queen. All I can recall is that it was a jumble of words ... it was all rather boring to a small child

David Morse had clearer memories of listening to the recording:

There was total silence - that is, a loud continuous scratching for the first few minutes, then a short sentence in a female voice, of which one word was 'tomatoes', then further mechanical scratching until the end. I always understood that Queen Victoria, like most people not professional actors, who are asked to 'say something,' simply so that their voices shall be heard and not for any purpose of communicating, was very shy when faced with a large horn which she had to address, and was only cajoled into speech when the recording time was nearly over by my (necessarily silent) grandfather indicating various objects in the room which might provoke a comment of some sort from Her Majesty.

I should say that when I heard the record I was old enough to know about gramophones and records but not sufficiently mature to be trusted with the archaic machine. It was played for me by my Aunt Enid or my elder brother, certainly not by my grandfather. I expect I was about 13. The occasion certainly took place at 14 Airlie Gardens, in fact in the first floor drawing room, and I remember on other occasions seeing the gramophone [sic] in the attic when we were up there in pursuit of some other property, luggage and the like.

David Morse was thirteen years old in 1922. No. 14 Airlie Gardens, Kensington, was Sydney and Juliet's London home from some time before the First World War until 1929; Juliet remained there until her own death in 1937. David Morse remembered it as:

...a large house with attics full of all sorts of stored relics. All Sydney's children used the house as their depot when in London; they and their wives (Enid never married) and children were familiar with much of the contents of the house.

David Morse remembered another of the Morses's frequent visitors: Diana Holman-Hunt, granddaughter of the William Holman Hunt, one of the founders of the Pre-Raphaelite Brotherhood, a small band of young men who set out to challenge the accepted standards of Victorian art. Holman Hunt's lesser known works included a chalk portrait of Sydney Morse. The wide circle of friends of the Holman Hunt and Morse families included Sir Joseph Swan's son Kenneth, who was Diana's godfather. In 1980, one visit to the Morses' home was especially prominent in Diana's memory:

> I certainly heard Queen Victoria's voice at Airlic Gardens. When sent to boarding school in the early Twenties (I was far too young to have been subjected to such an ordeal) the school of about thirty pupils was marched off in a crocodile to hear a voice on a crystal set in the village hall. We paid sixpence each for this privilege, which only lasted for two minutes. When I described this to my grandmother and Mama Morse, as Juliet Morse was known by my family, she said that I could hear Queen Victoria's voice. This was much clearer than the quacking of a talking duck which, with earphones clamped to my head, I heard in the village hall.

Having established that the recording survived into the 1920s, I now investigated its fate after Sydney Morse's death in January 1929; everything now hinged on the way in which his possessions were disposed of when his Will was proven on May 3rd, 1929 and probate granted to his executors, L.G.E. Morse and J.A.V. Morse. John Holgate recalled that one of these possessions was "a Phonograph, which until Morse died was in the general office at Alder House." He gave further details:

> It was like a treadle sewing machine. On it was screwed the Esco copying machine through which letters were copied. One day, shortly after Sydney Morse died, Esmond Morse when visiting the office saw the machine and said that he had been looking for it. The copier was removed and when the case of the machine was opened the phonograph with some cylinders was inside. My recollection is that Esmond said that it was wanted by the Victoria & Albert Museum. Whether or not it went there I do not know, but it went from the office.

Almost everyone on the east side of the Atlantic who has not studied the history of recording machines uses the word 'Phonograph' when referring to any type of cylinder record player, but by describing the machine at Alder House as being 'like a treadle sewing machine' John Holgate had virtually confirmed that it was an 1888 Graphophone, which was a foot-operated cylinder player driven by a treadle similar to those fitted to early sewing machines. Was the Graphophone that Sydney Morse kept at his office, its original purpose evidently forgotten by 1929, the machine that he had taken to Balmoral Castle in 1888? Or, if not, was it one of the machines that Henry Edmunds had demonstrated to the Royal Society of Arts?

It was now evident that the recording of Queen Victoria was still being played in the 1920s, and that one of Sydney's Graphophones and some of his cylinders were still in existence after January 1929. Would the trail now lead to what mattered most: the discovery of the sound of Queen Victoria's voice, immortalized amidst mechanical scratches on a wax-coated cardboard tube?

More clues were discovered in a correspondence file (Sc.M.3274) at the Science Museum. This proved that John Holgate's recollection of Esmond Morse's visit to Alder House to collect the Graphophone was correct, for on May 16th, 1929 (thirteen days after Probate on Sydney Morse's Will had been granted) Esmond wrote this letter to the Curator of the Victoria & Albert Museum:

> I have been deputed to take charge of and dispose of a number of scientific articles which were the property of my father, Mr Sydney Morse, who was at one time a member of the Council of the Institution of Electrical Engineers. The most interesting of these is a Graphophone, one of the first two or three imported from America, and my father demonstrated this to Queen Victoria in about the year 1878. There are also a few interesting records of about that date. Another item of interest is a number of specimens of incandescent electric light bulbs, in various stages of manufacture, which were prepared for and used in the Edison-Lane Fox Patent Case, and dated round about 1886. I am in a position to present these and some other similar objects to the Mu-

CONTRACTORS TO H.M. GOVERNMENT.

Science Mus- 21 MAY 1929

TELEGRAMS:
"PROPSOTUS, BATTPARK,
LONDON."

TELEPHONE:
BRIXTON 2117.
PRIVATE BRANCH EXCHANGE.

THE PROJECTILE & ENGINEERING COMPANY, LIMITED.

NEW ROAD,

LONDON, S.W. 8.   16th May, 1929

OFFICES & WORKS:
ACRE STREET,
NEW ROAD,
WANDSWORTH ROAD.

TRAMS: 26 FROM EMBANKMENT.
28 FROM VICTORIA.
BUSES: 77 FROM KING'S CROSS & EUSTON. TO SALVIN STREET.
177 TRAFALGAR SQUARE
WESTMINSTER BRIDGE.

RAILWAY STATIONS:
PASSENGER: SOUTHERN RLY. VAUXHALL (WESTERN SECTION) 1 MILE.
WANDSWORTH ROAD (CENTRAL SECTION) ½ MILE.
GOODS: WANDSWORTH ROAD. L. M. & S. RLY.
SOUTH LAMBETH. G. W. RLY.
NINE ELMS. SOUTHERN RLY.

SCIENCE MUSEUM

21 MAY 1929

Sc.M. 3274/1/1

The Curator,
    Victoria & Albert Museum,
      South Kensington.   S.W.7

Dear Sir,

      I have been deputed to take charge of and dispose of a number of scientific articles which were the property of my Father, Mr. Sydney Morse, who was at one time a member of the Council of the Institution of Electrical Engineers. The most interesting of these is a Graphophone, one of the first two or three imported from America, and my Father demonstrated this to Queen Victoria in about the year 1878. There are also a few interesting records of about that date.

      Another item of interest is a number of specimens of incandescent electric light bulbs, in various stages of manufacture, which were prepared for and used in the Edison-Lane Fox Patent Case, and dated round about 1886.

      I am in a position to present these, and some other similar objects to the Museum, if suitable arrangements can be made for their reception, and I should be glad to call and discuss the matter with you if you are interested.

      Yours faithfully,

Esmond Morse's letter to the Victoria & Albert Museum, offering to present a Graphophone and other scientific articles to the Museum.

seum, if suitable arrangements can be made for
their reception.

Clearly, the date 1878 for Sydney Morse's demonstration
of the Graphophone to Queen Victoria is either a typing error
in Esmond's letter, or an indication that he had only a vague
memory of what his father had told him about the demonstration. It is also possible that he was not particularly
interested in ancient recording apparatus. By 1929 electrical recordings, electric gramophones playing shellac discs
and, of course, "the wireless" were the latest forms of home
entertainment; Phonographs and cylinders were obsolete,
and the acoustic machines of yesteryear were of little use or
interest to anyone.

At the time of Sydney Morse's death, Esmond and his
family had recently moved from The Old Manor, Witley,
Surrey, to a new flat, 12 Brant House, Larkhall, Battersea, in
south-west London. Esmond was at this time manager of the
Projectile & Engineering Company of New Road, London,
SW8, and it was from here that he wrote to the Victoria &
Albert while disposing of his father's 'scientific articles.'
These would have been out of place among the Museum's
collection of fine and applied arts but Esmond's letter had
been forwarded to H.G. Lyons of the Science Museum, who
wrote to Esmond on May 28th, asking whether the officers in
charge of the Museum's electrical and recording machine
departments could inspect the articles on Thursday, June
6th.

Esmond's visit to Alder House was probably made a few
days before the visit of these officers. Whether or not Esmond
was already in possession of the other articles he had offered,
or had to collect them from 14 Airlie Gardens, is not known.

However, on June 6th, T. Hartley and Dr W.S. Plummer of the
Science Museum kept their appointment at 12 Brant House.
It appears that Esmond was absent, for they refer in their
report to conversations with a Miss Morse; this could have
been one of Esmond's two daughters or (more likely) Enid
Morse, Sydney and Juliet's daughter. From the electrical
items, Hartley recommended accepting six Edison lamps
and a Woodhouse & Ransom lamp and lampholder, none of
which was already represented in the Museum's collection.
On June 10th, Dr Plummer reported:

> The phonograph in question is a treadle model of
> about 1887-1893; unfortunately several vital parts
> are missing and Miss Morse has promised to
> search for them. Unless they can be found I would
> not recommend the acceptance of the instru-
> ment, but it might be well to accept two interesting
> accessories: (1) a very old Graphophone record
> cylinder of cardboard, about 8" long and 1" diam-
> eter, dating back as far as 1887, of which we have
> at present no example; (2) a wax cylinder record in
> which Queen Victoria speaks a few words. Miss
> Morse is trying to find the latter, and she will write
> as soon as possible concerning the matter.

Hartley and Dr Plummer reported to W.Spencer and
Captain H. Shaw respectively at the Science Museum, and
on June 10th, Shaw wrote to Spencer:

> So far as the Graphophone is concerned it is
> unfortunately incomplete, otherwise it would be a
> very desirable exhibit, but unless the missing
> Museum. The cardboard cylindrical record should
> certainly be accepted as it is the predecessor of

the wax record, and is not represented in the collection. The wax record is interesting as being a record of Queen Victoria's voice but from the Museum point of view has no further claim to a place here. It is doubtful whether we should accept it, and I think perhaps it would be desirable to decline the offer of this record.

By June 18th, all four officers had decided what should be accepted. On Saturday, June 22th, Lyons wrote to Esmond Morse:

With reference to your kind offer to present an early Graphophone and a number of early incandescent lamps for exhibition at this Museum, I shall be very pleased to accept the seven lamps and one lamp holder which were selected, and also the cardboard Graphophone cylinder. If agreeable to you, I will arrange to collect these objects early next week. I regret I am unable to accept the Graphophone in its present condition as it is too incomplete, but should the missing parts be found I should be most grateful if you would allow me to accept it as the model is one of considerable historic interest.

Lyons and his officers missed an important opportunity during their discussions and correspondence with Esmond Morse, for surely they should have accepted the Graphophone "as seen," in the hope that its missing parts would eventually be found and donated to the Museum?

The possibility of obtaining the components by "cannibalizing" another incomplete Graphophone at some time in the

22nd June, 1929.

So.M.3274/1/2.

Sir,

With reference to your kind offer to present an early Graphophone and a number of early incandescent electric lamps for exhibition in this Museum, I shall be very pleased to accept the seven lamps and one lamp holder which were selected, and also the cardboard Graphophone record cylinder. If agreeable to you, I will arrange to collect these objects early next week.

I regret that I am unable to accept the Graphophone in its present condition as it is too incomplete, but should the missing parts be found, I should be most grateful if you would allow me to accept it as the model is one of considerable historic interest.

I am, Sir,

Your obedient Servant,

H. G. LYONS.

Director.

Osmond Morse, Esq.,
12, Brant House,
Larkhall,
S.W.8.

The culmination of Esmond Morse's correspondence with the Science Museum - a letter from the Director accepting various objects, including the Graphophone cylinder.

future, should Esmond and Miss Morse have failed to find the original parts, would also have justified accepting the machine. Today, it seems curious that the chance to acquire a recording machine that had been demonstrated to Queen Victoria was lost. What is even more puzzling is that Captain Shaw rejected the offer of a recording of Queen Victoria's voice. Admittedly at the time that Hartley and Dr Plummer visited 12 Brant House they were told that the cylinder had been mislaid but Shaw made it obvious, in his note to Spencer, that he would not be in favour of accepting it, even if it could be found. Nor, apparently, was Esmond Morse put in touch with the Royal Archivist at Windsor Castle or curators of other museums likely to be interested in a recording machine and recording so intimately associated with Queen Victoria.

Until I embarked on my research in the 1980s, only one previous effort had been made since 1929 to discover what became of the 'Queen Victoria cylinder'. In October 1964, Lord Tangley, then Sydney Morse & Co's senior partner, read the Countess of Longford's book *Victoria R.I.* and was prompted by the description of Sydney's visit to Balmoral Castle to make enquiries about it, and tell Lady Longford of Esmond Morse's offer to donate the Graphophone and various cylinders to the Science Museum. Lady Longford replied to Lord Tangley, saying that she would like to see the instrument and the records, if this could be arranged. Lord Tangley also discovered that after Sydney's death not only was his Graphophone found in his office, but also some of Sir Joseph Swan's original carbon filament lamps, bearing handwritten identification marks applied by Sir Frederick Bramwell, the eminent Victorian consulting engineer and a noted advocate, witness and arbitrator. Bramwell had been President of the British Association in 1888, the year when Henry Edmunds introduced the Graphophone at the BA's annual meeting; Bramwell and Morse handled many of the electrical pioneers' patent cases and other legal affairs. Lord Tangley also found that among the recordings Esmond Morse offered the Science Museum was one of Queen Victoria's pipers, recorded at Balmoral; it seems likely that this record, and the one of Queen Victoria's voice, were among the cylinders that were found when the case beneath the Graphophone was opened on that day in 1929 when Esmond Morse called at Alder House to collect the machine.

Unaware of what had happened after Hartley and Dr Plummer visited Esmond's home on June 6th, 1929, Lord Tangley wrote to the Science Museum in February 1965, giving details of Esmond Morse's offer and hoping to arrange for Lady Longford to see the Graphophone and the recordings made at Balmoral. V.K. Chew, assistant keeper in the department of physics, re-opened file no. Sc.M.3274 and replied to Lord Tangley, saying that the Museum had not accepted the Graphophone or the "wax recording containing a few words spoken by Queen Victoria" because of the lack of "certain essential components" in the Graphophone and the fact that the recording, "although of great human interest, displayed no noteworthy technical features." Evidently, Lord Tangley discussed V.K. Chew's reply with Esmond Morse, for on February 16th, 1965, Lord Tangley wrote again, saying:

> Mr Esmond Morse's recollection is that he could not find this record and we should be obliged if you would let us know whether in fact your records do show that the one of Queen Victoria's

voice was not accepted by the Museum

V.K. Chew replied:

> I have consulted the relevant records and find
> that the Queen Victoria record was not specifi-
> cally mentioned when Mr Morse first wrote to offer
> certain objects to the Museum. It was mentioned
> however when a Museum officer called to inspect
> these objects but it could not then be found and
> it was arranged that the Museum should be
> notified if it came to light. It was then decided that
> the record would not be accepted even if found ...
> the letter to Mr Morse accepting some of the
> objects offered did not however mention the record,
> and it would appear therefore that either it was
> not found or the Museum was not notified that it
> had been found.

It appears that after Lord Tangley concluded his correspondence with V.K. Chew, neither he nor Esmond made any
further attempt to trace Sydney Morse's Graphophone and
cylinders. Christie's catalogues of the sale of his property on
July 26th, 1929 and of Juliet Morse's property on March
19th, 1937 (she died on January 9th that year) do not list any
recording machines or cylinders. An insurance valuation
containing an inventory of the contents of 14 Airlie Gardens,
prepared in 1930, mentions a "cabinet gramophone" but this
description does not fit that of the missing Graphophone.
Esmond Morse died on March 7th, 1970.

The Science Museum's correspondence with Esmond
Morse in 1929 and Lord Tangley in 1965 almost led me to
assume that the "Queen Victoria recording" was lost forever,

but I was deterred from abandoning my search after I noticed a curious anomaly in Dr Plummer's report of June 10th, 1929. Dr Plummer described the recording as *a wax cylinder*, as if to make it clear that it was noticeably different in appearance to the Graphophone record, which he described as being made of *cardboard and measuring about eight inches in length and one inch in diameter*. Dr Plummer's colleague, Captain Shaw, was also careful to differentiate between the "cardboard cylindrical record" and the "wax record." Although Esmond Morse had told the museum that he had "a few interesting records" we can perhaps assume, in the absence of a detailed list of what he had to offer, that on the day of Plummer and Hartley's visit, only one Graphophone cylinder was available for their inspection; what they did not realize was that, even if the wax cylinder could be found, it could not possibly have been the recording made by Queen Victoria in 1888!

The reason for this is obvious now, but did not occur to the Science Museum's officers in 1929: Queen Victoria did not record her voice on a "wax cylinder" but on *a wax-coated cardboard cylinder* - perhaps the very one that was inspected by Dr Plummer on June 6th, taken to the Science Museum sometime during the week ending June 29th, but apparently never played since the day it was received there.

To explain why Dr Plummer and his colleagues thought that Queen Victoria's voice was immortalized on wax, not on a wax coating, it is necessary to review the 'state of the art' in sound recording in the mid-1880s, when Edison was improving his Phonograph in response to the challenge of the Graphophone. Instead of recording on a piece of tinfoil wound around a cylinder, Edison's new machine recorded on cylinders made from a prepared wax compound. The walls of the cylinder were about a quarter of an inch thick, allowing them to be repeatedly shaved so that old recordings could be erased and new ones made in their place. Edison called his record a *Phonogram*. The inventors of the *Graphophone*, on the other hand, developed a cylinder of wax coated cardboard, which could only be used once. Because of its thin walls it was very different to Edison's more substantial wax cylinders.

From Dr Plummer's report I knew that he recognized a Graphophone cylinder when he saw one. He did not see the other cylinder, but there is a tantalizing possibility that whoever told him that it was a wax cylinder, described it as such (perhaps in response to specific questions put by Dr Plummer) because he or she wanted to make the point that it was different to the cylinder that was available at that moment for Plummer's inspection. And if the lost cylinder was an Edison Phonogram, then Esmond and Enid Morse were mistaken in thinking that it was the one on which Queen Victoria had recorded her voice.

Had there been, in the aftermath of Sydney Morse's death, a favourable misunderstanding over the identity of the cylinder? Had he placed it, years previously, in the case of the Graphophone at his office, for safe keeping, only for it to be given to the Science Museum, its true value unknown?

More than fifty years later, in October 1980, Dr D.B. Thomas, Keeper of the Museum's physics department, searched for, and found, the cylinder given to his predecessors by Esmond Morse. It had been kept in various cupboards since 1929, its possible significance unsuspected. Eight inches long and one and a quarter inches in diameter,

Dr D.B. Thomas with the Graphophone cylinder after it had been traced to the Science Museum in 1980.

The Graphophone cylinder that Esmond Morse gave to the Science Museum.

it bore an inventory number, 1929-607 (applied at the time it was accepted by the Museum) and had three widely-spaced bands of grooves, suggesting that someone at one time made three separate recordings on it. The Museum did not have a Graphophone and was unable to play the record. It was however, examined under a stereo-microscope. The indentations or engravings formed by the recording stylus in the grooves of cylindrical or disc records are usually visible, but no such marks could be seen on this cylinder. Nevertheless, the mystery of why, when and where an attempt was made to record on the cylinder remained. Told of the results of the microscopic examination, David Morse thought back again to the time he heard the Queen Victoria cylinder and commented:

> There is nothing recorded for at least the first half, and the few words then spoken finish some considerable distance before the end.

Because the Science Museum was unwilling to entrust the cylinder to any kind of makeshift playback apparatus, I attempted to find a Graphophone which the Museum could borrow in order to play the record. Comparatively few Graphophones were built and those that survive are in other museums or private collections. A 'transitional' Graphophone, made in about 1893 and capable of playing Graphophone cylinders and Edison Phonograms, was sold at Christie's in 1980 for £5,000. However, at that time it had only a sound reproducer for Phonograms; in any case, the machine could not be traced because its buyer had asked to remain anonymous. In the summer of 1982, while I was attempting to locate a suitable Graphophone, I contacted Christopher Proudfoot of Christie's mechanical department and editor of the City of London Phonograph and Gramophone Society's magazine *Hillandale News*, who advised against playing the cylinder on an acoustic machine; a machine (such as old cylinder-type Dictaphone) with an electric pick-up and an appropriate stylus would, he said, be more suitable for a cylinder of such possible importance.

Told of the three bands of grooves on the otherwise smooth cylinder, Christopher Proudfoot commented:

> Certainly [they] indicate that an attempt has been made to record on it; grooves would be cut by the recording stylus whether or not anyone spoke into the mouthpiece, as might happen if a diffident performer were having difficulty in finding anything to say.

David Morse's comments about loud scratching, a short sentence containing the word "tomatoes" and Queen Victoria being cajoled into speech when the recording time was nearly over, immediately came to mind. I also wondered if whatever sounds that had been directed at the cylinder had been so faint that they had failed to create any impressions that were likely to be visible under a microscope; or, alternatively, that any impressions that might at one time have been visible were now masked by the effects of "old age" - shrinkage or crazing - on the cylinder's surface.

I also received encouragement from another source that although the cylinder did not display any signs of having been used to record someone's voice, it might yield some recognisable sounds if actually played. At that time I was writing a biography of John Montagu, the 2nd Lord Montagu of Beaulieu, who like Henry Edmunds had been a motoring pioneer in the 1890s. I told John's son Edward, the present

Lord Montagu, about the discovery of the cylinder and the negative results when it was examined under a microscope. Lord Montagu wrote to Dame Margaret Weston, director of the Science Museum, offering to arrange for the cylinder to be played on a suitable instrument. On July 12th, 1982, Dr Thomas replied on Dame Margaret's behalf:

> ...although we would very much like to find the Queen Victoria recording, we cannot see any signs of a recording on the cylinder. However hill and dale recordings are not always easy to see and I have used the same microscope to look at other playable recordings and found that the quiet passages can be difficult to see. We do not have a Graphophone which can play the cylinder and we would be interested in locating such an instrument in this country. The cylinders are quite rare and so I would not like to send the only cylinder of this type we have abroad with the expectation that there is no recording on it.

Now that I knew that optical examination of the cylinder could not be regarded as infallible proof that no sound impressions were present on it, I wrote to Dame Margaret Weston, suggesting that the Science Museum should seek help from Professor Walter Welch of the Sound Archives Laboratory at Syracuse University, N.Y. George Frow had told me that the university had developed equipment with which to process old cylinders on which the voices of famous people had been recorded. Dame Margaret passed my letter to Dr Thomas, who replied on July 29th, 1982:

> I am a bit reluctant to get the cylinder played because, as you know, it was not believed to be

the Queen Victoria recording when it was presented to us and does not appear to have any recording whatsoever on it.

While I was writing the first chapters of my book about Henry Edmunds, I came across press reports that reminded me that sooner or later I would have to try again to get someone to play the cylinder. Dr Thomas's comments to Lord Montagu about quiet passages being difficult to see kept coming to mind, and various newspaper reports made me optimistic that, one day, the cylinder would be played. In December 1987 an article by Nigel Andrew in *The Times* included these encouraging words:

> Several ... eminent Victorians got themselves on to wax cylinders in the 1880s. Distorted and indistinct, they still speak to us across 100 years, thanks to the National Sound Archive. The archive is at present on the brink of a technological revolution, as it begins work with the Computer Enhanced Digital Audio Restoration System. The results, I am assured, will be little more than miraculous.

Soon after this report appeared it was announced that a method of using a laser beam, instead of a stylus, to play conventional long-playing records, was being developed; if this could be applied to cylinders, it would enable the impressions imparted by the recording stylus to be decoded without being touched. There was also speculation that the grooves on the sides of ancient Egyptian clay vases and bowls would one day yield the conversations and songs of the craftsmen who made them, thousands of years ago; theoretically at least, the tools used to shape and form the vessels as they spun on the potters' wheels could have acted like recording styluses, and recorded the hubbub of the workshop in the surface of the clay!

Further news of astonishing developments in audio technology that were being achieved or forecast came in May 1988, when Robert Matthews, technology correspondent for *The Times*, reported:

> A machine about to be unveiled by the National Sound Archive promises to make 100-year-old recordings sound as if they were made yesterday. The machine takes advantage of research in digital signal processing of the type used in defence ... sounds from worn or broken recordings are sampled 40,000 times a second as the machine turns them into a stream of numbers. The 'digitised' result is fed into a computer. Mathematical imitations of sounds of musical instruments and voices have been developed, enabling the computer to estimate what sounds have been lost by scratches and cracks. The computer fills in the damage. Noises generated by cracks can be removed and surface noise almost totally removed. Cleaned up recordings are stored on tape. The machine takes many hours to process a single record, but researchers believe it should be possible to do the job in under three hours.

During the summer of 1990, I decided that the time had come for the another attempt to get mute and mysterious cylinder number 1929-607 played. Clearly, astonishing progress in audio technology had been made in the eight years that had passed since I last corresponded with the

Science Museum. Surely, developments such as laser scanning or digital computing would offer an answer to the problem of playing and analysing a Graphophone cylinder whose grooves appeared to be unimpressed by the sound of a human voice? Would today's 'state of the art' audio equipment now enable Sydney Morse's cylinder to speak to us from the Victorian past - and would we then hear the voice of the most eminent Victorian of all? Even if all that emerged was the word 'tomatoes', the computer's time would not have been wasted.

I decided to seek advice from the National Sound Archive, which is one of the largest sound archives in the world and has collections dating back to the 1890s - but not, I noted, to the time when the type of cylinder in which I was interested was introduced. On June 4th, 1990, I wrote to the National Sound Archive. I explained that I had located a cylinder containing what might be a recording made by Queen Victoria, and asked whether they could play it. Benet Bergonzi, Curator of Artefacts, replied that the cylinder could be transcribed, or some idea of its contents obtained, by playing it on an "electronic phonograph" built by the National Sound Archive's engineer some years ago. I immediately wrote to Dr Derek Robinson, head of science in the Science Museum's collections management division, telling him about my research and requesting that the National Sound Archive should play the cylinder. A few weeks later it was taken to the National Sound Archive - a few hundred yards from the Science Museum - but I soon seemed to be heading back to where I started nearly ten years earlier. Benet Bergonzi wrote:

Optical examination by our conservation manager, Peter Copeland, suggested no sound was present on the cylinder (the grooves being unmodulated) but we could not play it because our electronic phonograph's mandrel will take only 2¼ in. diameter Edison style cylinders. A suitable mandrel is being specially made in the Science Museum's workshops and when this is ready the cylinder will be played. However, if there is any sound on the cylinder it is likely to be too quiet for recognition or comprehension.

Because of their intense rivalry the inventors of the Phonograph and the Bell-Tainter Graphophone had made no attempt to make their recording cylinders compatible with each other's recording machines in 1888. The important difference, so far as the National Sound Archive was concerned in 1990, is that the internal bore (i.e. the hole through the centre) of early Graphophone cylinders is one and one-eighth of an inch in diameter. This is half the diameter of the bore of Edison's Phonograph cylinders. The Graphophone cylinder was the first of its type that the National Sound Archive had ever been asked to play, and therefore Peter Copeland had never before needed a compatible mandrel. It was not until June 11th, 1991 that this and other problems were overcome and cylinder number 1929-607 - which by now I was optimistically calling 'the Queen Victoria cylinder' - was played for the first time for more than 60 years. In the early 1890s the original Bell-Tainter Graphophone-type cylinder went out of production and Graphophone machines capable of playing only Edison-standard cylinders were introduced. I knew, therefore, that the cylinder was made sometime before the early 1890s, but when were the bands of grooves inscribed on it? I had to bear in mind that at any time during his later life, Sydney Morse might have dusted off his old Graphophone, found a blank cylinder - and attempted to make another record.

Before setting up his modified electronic Phonograph, Peter Copeland examined the cylinder visually, for the second time. Despite its age it was in excellent condition, although its ozokerite mineral paraffin wax surface was quite brittle. The three bands of grooves contained nothing to indicate when they were inscribed, or how often the cylinder had been played during the time it belonged to Sydney Morse.

I had assumed that the equipment on which the cylinder would be played would scan the grooves by means of a laser beam or a very fine stylus, in order not to damage the grooves. Peter Copeland had, in fact, momentarily considered sending the cylinder to a laboratory in Japan which has one of the few laser scanners capable of reading cylinder recordings. He rejected this idea because published reports have indicated that the process enhances the surface noise as well as the recording, so the National Sound Archive's first attempt to coax sound from the cylinder was made with the aid of a lightweight pick-up, made in the 1960s, fitted with a coarse stylus similar to those which were commercially available in the days of 78 r.p.m. gramophone records. Peter Copeland chose this stylus because its blunt elliptical tip was less likely to damage the cylinder - so much for my assumption that a fine stylus would be safer! The possibility that, despite careful preparations, the cylinder would withstand only one playback, could not be discounted, so in order to capture whatever signals came from the grooves, the phonograph was connected to a reel-to-reel tape deck running ¼ in. wide magnetic tape at 15 inches a second, and the signal from the cylinder was transferred to the tape via a Packburn noise suppressor. Witnessed by Stephanie Millard from the Science Museum and Benet Bergonzi, Peter switched on the tape deck and recorded details of what he was about to do - "I'm starting off at 80 r.p.m. because I have no idea what's going to happen."

The cylinder revolved, the stylus was lowered on to its surface, and the witnesses huddled round a loudspeaker that had been set up to allow the playback to be heard "live."

The result: seventeen seconds of extremely loud surface noise but, among the scratches, the sound of someone whistling followed by an almost inaudible deep voice.

Before playing any more tracks, Peter stopped the phonograph and announced that the cylinder was running too slowly. He also found that the cylinder was running backwards, this being evident because no vowel sounds were audible and the voice's cadences were rising, instead of falling. The reversal of the cylinder was due to the fact that the first Graphophone cylinders were symmetrical. It is not possible, merely by looking at a cylinder, to tell at which end its recording starts, so there is a 50:50 chance of slipping it on to its mandrel the wrong way round. Edison prevented this happening on his Phonographs by tapering their mandrels and the bore of their cylinders, so that they had to be fitted together correctly, but owners of Graphophones had to devise their own way of marking where their records started. In this particular case, Sydney Morse had omitted to do this.

Peter Copeland turned the cylinder round, increased the speed of rotation to 160 r.p.m. and ran, in the opposite direction, the band he had first played. This time a man could

The Electronic Phonograph machine at the National Sound Archive.
Sydney Morse's Graphophone cylinder is mounted on the mandrel.

be heard half-singing, half-reciting the phrase "Now how is this today," placing equal emphasis on all six syllables, so that the word 'today' came over as "too-day". The words were immediately followed by about twelve whistled notes. However, a man's voice was not what everyone was hoping to hear and interest mounted as Peter played Band Two and then what should have been called Band One in the first place - the band at what had now been identified as being nearest to the "start" end of the cylinder. To prevent any confusion, the "whistling" track was renamed Band Three.

During the next fourteen seconds there emerged, from the depths of the grooves of Band Two, another voice, unmistakably that of a woman but barely audible and certainly too faint to enable anyone to hear any words, let alone a complete phrase or sentence. Band One was longer - twenty-one seconds - but although its sounds consisted almost entirely of excruciating surface noise there were a few snatches of a woman's voice, almost beyond the range of the human ear.

Peter Copeland added his comments to the master tape: "If Queen Victoria is going to be on this cylinder at all, it sounds as though it's going to be Band Two. I suspect that Band One is an essentially unmodulated test cut and so let's concentrate on Band Two." He surmised that 160 r.p.m. had been rather too fast a speed for the previous transcription and now slowed the phonograph to 140 r.p.m.. From the next test, it sounded as if the woman spoke about 40 words or syllables, although the only ones that could be recognized were "Greetings ... that the answer can be ... and I've never forgotten." Peter slowed the machine to 130 r.p.m. and, to clarify the vowel sounds, added additional filters. Previously the bandwidth of the transcriptions had been limited between 220

Benet Bergonzi (left) and Peter Copeland of the National Sound Archive prepare to play the transcription of the Graphophone recording.

Peter Copeland and Benet Bergonzi play the transcription.

hertz and 3160 hertz. Now, he cut an extra octave from the bottom of the range, and an extra one from the top, limiting the bandwidth to 440 hertz - 1660 hertz. The result, although better, did not enable any more words to be picked out, so a further transcription was made, this time with a finer stylus - one with a spherical tip 1/1000th of an inch in diameter - and additional treble and bass filters. The surface noise was now less distracting but the "lost" words were still indistinct.

To complete the session, Peter transcribed Band One and Band Three without making any further adjustments. The voice on Band One was now louder than before and sounded like the same woman who had been heard on Band Two. During this test, Band Three was inevitably transcribed backwards - the whistled tune came first, in reverse, and "Now how is this too (sic) day" became a series of grunts.

Afterwards, Peter commented that the dynamics of the recordings on bands one and two - especially their similar speeds -suggested that they had both been recorded on the same occasion. Band Three had been recorded at a significantly different speed and sounded as if it had been made on a different occasion - though it was not possible to say whether this was before or after the one at which the woman's voice was recorded. This theory was supported by the fact that the cylinder had obviously been taken off its mandrel and used the "wrong" way round at some time during its brief life as a recording medium. Peter also speculated that the consistency of the recording speed - especially during the whistled passage - suggested that the Graphophone used on both occasions was motor-driven or governed, not hand-cranked like many of the first cylinder players. The speed in any one band varied by no more than five per cent.

It was not possible to decide whether the high levels of surface noise on the three bands were due to poor signal to noise ratios at the time the recordings were made, or to scratches created on the cylinder when it was played back during the time it belonged to Sydney Morse.

The transcriptions made on June 11th were the best that could be achieved with the National Sound Archive's equipment and so it was decided to copy, on to digital audio tape, the transcription of Band Two that had been made at 130 r.p.m.. The tape was sent to Cedar Audio Ltd of Cambridge, a company that is in the forefront of audio technology. Cedar filtered the track and eliminated the "clicks" and "thumps" that had made Band Two so difficult to listen to and interpolated, in their place, a signal of the same waveform as that of the voice that had been overwhelmed by these noises.

The result was a dramatic improvement on the National Sound Archive's succession of 'cleaned up' transcriptions. It became evident that the voice is that of a well-educated, upper class woman - she sounds not unlike H. M. Queen Elizabeth II - but although the "Cedarized" tracks make Band Two less of an assault on the ear, they do not enable any more words to be distinguished. Certainly the word "tomatoes" that David Morse heard in the 1920s has not emerged, although it may be in the still-inaudible passages in Band Two or somewhere in Band One, the processing of which by Cedar Audio will have to wait until the National Sound Archive can fund further work. Other aspects of bands one and two bear resemblanceS to what David Morse had heard - "loud continuous scratching", "a short sentence in a female voice", "nothing recorded for at least the first half and the few words then spoken finish some considerable distance before the end."

Certainly, so far as Band Two is concerned, it seems that all that can be done by the world's most advanced equipment, has been done. It will probably not be possible to make Band Two any clearer until there is another advance in audio technology - almost inevitable in the light of what has happened in the past few years. Alternatively, perhaps syllable-by-syllable analysis of the transcription on a hand-indexed tape deck by someone with sufficient experience - and patience - may yield a few more phrases. If some complete sentences can be reconstructed, historians may be able to decide whether they refer to any known aspect of Queen Victoria's life in 1888, or to her Jubilee the previous year.

Fortunately cylinder number 1929-607 withstood the transcription process - the styluses dislodged small particles of ozokerite from its surface, but not enough to prevent the bands being tracked again. So, if necessary, future researchers will be able to listen to the cylinder, although they will probably prefer to analyse the transcriptions that were copied on to digital audio tape. Certainly, the more people who listen to the transcriptions, the better, since others may hear something their predecessors have missed. No two pairs of ears are identical. For example, one listener thought he heard the woman say "Greetings, Britons and everybody" at the beginning of Band Two, although others have not been able to make out the words immediately after "Greetings". Perhaps someone with exceptionally sensitive hearing - a blind person, for example - would have more success?

I played Cedar Audio's transcription of Band Two to Diana Holman-Hunt but she did not recognize the voice. Before this book went to press I just had time to copy the transcription on to compact cassettes and send these to Mary Barton and David Morse. It was, perhaps, asking too much to expect anyone to say whether the faint, scratch-masked voice they were listening to in 1991 was the one they had heard on a primitive recording machine in their childhood in the 1920s. Mary Barton said:

> I can't definitely confirm this is what I heard my grandfather play in the early 1920s but it easily might be.

Later she wrote to me and said:

> It certainly sounds like the recording I heard during the 1920s but that's a long time ago and one's memory may be blurred after so long, and anyway, as I would only have been 8-10 years old, I may have been interested in other things!

David Morse prefaced his response with a further recollection of what he heard on the "Queen Victoria" recording:

> There was a long pause, perhaps half the total extent of the transmission, a total silence, and then some encouraging words in a male voice and then a high female voice saying "tomatoes" and then silence 'til the end of the transmission. On the present transmission which you sent me there is so much scratch that the words of the female voice cannot be distinguished and since what you sent me is only a copy, one cannot assess from it whether there is a long gap in the original before there is any speech at all, which would indicate whether the original from which

The equipment used by Ceder Audio of Cambridge to analyse the recordings.

your copy is taken is in fact the record … in which
we are interested.

There is in fact a gap of four seconds before the woman says "Greetings". On Band One there is a gap of about nine seconds before the voice is heard. It will be interesting to obtain David Morse's opinion of this band when it is "Cedarized".

CONCLUSION

The main difficulties faced when trying to decide whether the woman speaking on the cylinder is Queen Victoria is that no comparison can be made with proven recordings of her voice, - there are none. Indeed, if there were any, cylinder number 1929-607 would not be of such potential importance: nor is there anyone alive today who might have met the Queen and be able to recall the sound of her voice.

So what did Queen Victoria sound like? As a child, she spoke nothing but German until she was three years old, when she began to learn English. It is sometimes said that all through her life she spoke with a German or guttural accent but this does not appear to be true. In her book *Victoria R.I.*, Lady Longford wrote:

> With her good ear [Victoria] mastered it [English] without a trace of German accent. There was a precision and clarity about her pronunciation, however, which some people found exquisite while others called it refined.*

Lady Longford also described how the Queen's voice sounded in 1887, her Golden Jubilee year, when she was 68 years old. On June 22nd hundreds of pupils from Eton gathered at Windsor Castle and sang their school song to her. Lady Longford wrote:

> ...when she said in her clear, musical voice, 'I thank you very much,' the applause was deafening.§

Despite the poor quality of cylinder number 1929-607, the voice does have a certain precision, a clarity of pronuncia-

* Weidenfeld and Nicolson, 1964.
§ Ibid.

tion, a suggestion of refinement and a clear, musical quality. If it is a recording of Queen Victoria, it was made within seventeen months of the Etonians' serenade. Her voice is unlikely to have lost its distinctive quality by the late summer and autumn of 1888, even though she was by now 69 years old.

It must be said, though, that there were many other well-spoken ladies who could have recorded their voices for Sydney Morse at around this time.

Many questions still remain unanswered and perhaps unanswerable. I was puzzled by Peter Copeland's conclusion that the Graphophone on which cylinder number 1929-607 was recorded was motor driven or governed. I already knew that the Graphophone demonstrated by Henry Edmunds to the British Association for the Advancement of Science was driven by a foot treadle. So far as I was aware, no motor driven or hand-cranked Graphophones were imported into Britain by Henry Edmunds and Sydney Morse, although such models were being used in the USA at that time. Turning again to reports of Henry's demonstration to the B.A. I read: "The machine regulates its own speed by means of an ingenious but simple governor" and (verbatim, from his talk) "An ordinary treadle like a sewing machine rotates a speed governor. This by a leather belt communicates a constant speed to the ... cylinder".

Later, I learned from George Frow that the governor was a mechanism consisting of a fly-weight and slip clutch, and was intended to hold the recording speed at 40 r.p.m. - enabling up to 700 words to be recorded on a cylinder. Obviously, whoever assembled the Graphophone before recording the woman's voice on cylinder number 1929-607 did not set the governor correctly and allowed the machine to run at about 100 r.p.m. faster than its makers intended. The voice sounds natural on the transcriptions that were made when the cylinder was played at 140 r.p.m. and 130 r.p.m., and in my opinion this is likely to have been the approximate speed range when the original recording was made.

If the secrets of cylinder number 1929-607 are ever extracted, its voices and perhaps the whistling will reveal more about its origins than its technical features. Who is the man who says "Now how is this too (sic) day?" Is he a member of Queen Victoria's household, one of those who - according to Lady Longford - recorded whistles and German jokes before the Queen "spoke a few words"? Or is it Sydney Morse himself testing the machine? Admittedly, the man is heard on the cylinder after the woman's voice, and Peter Copeland thinks it likely that this band was recorded on a different occasion than the other two. We know that during Sydney's visit to Balmoral several recordings were made (by the Queen, her household and her pipers). The recording machine would probably have been set up several times, in which case it would have been easy - for the reason explained earlier - for cylinder number 1929-607 to have been run in one direction for two recordings, and in the opposite direction for a third, and for the speed governor to have been reset. If Sydney Morse was the operator of the machine for all three recordings on the cylinder, perhaps he had less experience than Henry Edmunds and made some elementary mistakes - without even realizing that he done so?

And why is the woman's voice on Band One so faint? Was this one made while Sydney was trying to persuade the Queen to say a few words? Was she, at this time, talking to someone across the room, and reluctant to hold the machine's funnel-shaped mouthpiece close enough to her lips to ensure that her words were properly recorded?

On Band Two it appears that the speaker's voice is being aimed more directly at the mouthpiece. But what possible words could connect "Greetings ... that the answer must be ... and I've never forgotten"? Answer to what? Never forgotten what? Is this, perhaps, not a spontaneous comment but a sentence or two read from a book, or from a letter that the Queen had received, or from one that she was writing? If this was the Queen, could she have been reminiscing? If so, about what? Her Golden Jubilee the previous year, or some other event during her long and eventful reign?

Since June 1991 I have played the transcriptions over and over again, and I am still fascinated by the possibility that the voice on bands one and two could be that of Queen Victoria. I also wonder whether the full story of Queen Victoria's encounter with the Graphophone has been handed down to us in Lady Longford's account of the Queen's "treats", in Henry Edmunds's reminiscences (written in the 1920s), and in what Sydney Morse told those who listened to the cylinder at Airlie Gardens.

Consider again what happened in 1888. Sydney Morse, whose wife and mother-in-law were friends of the Royal Family, went to Balmoral. He took with him - or forwarded - a cumbersome recording machine and, we assume, a generous supply of cylinders: blank ones, certainly, on which to make recordings at Balmoral, and presumably some pre-recorded ones too. These would have enabled him to convey messages to the Queen, entertain her with songs or recitations, or whatever, and demonstrate the full capabilities of the instrument. It is more than 550 miles from London to Ballater, the nearest railway station to Balmoral, so Sydney spent all day (or all night) on a train, and had to complete the last stage of his journey by horse-drawn carriage. The journey was long and tiring, and he would probably have been the Queen's guest for several days - she would hardly have expected him to pack his bags and return home after only a day or two. With plenty of time available, especially during the dark evenings, surely the Graphophone could have been used several times, to make recordings and replay them?

Surely, too, the Queen's curiosity would have induced her to speak more than a few words into the machine? Surely, too, out of consideration for Sydney Morse, she would have spoken for more than a few seconds, however shy she may have been the first time she was confronted by the recording machine?

If cylinder number 1929-607 was one of the cylinders that Sydney took to Balmoral, then perhaps it was only the first of a few on which the Queen recorded - the other cylinders having been destroyed, lost or forgotten by the time that Henry wrote about his Graphophone venture, and Sydney played his old recordings to his family and visitors at 14 Airlie Gardens. Alternatively, perhaps the cylinder bears a message to the Queen, or the voice of another guest at Balmoral, and is not the one that David Morse and Mary Barton heard in the 1920s.

We know that shortly before and soon after Sydney Morse died, several cylinders that belonged to him were still in existence, though exactly where they were all kept has not been established. Only cylinder number 1929-607 is known to have survived until now, but because Sydney was a promoter of Graphophones it is likely that there were other Graphophone cylinders in his collection. Unless they were deliberately or accidentally discarded after Sydney died, they may survive somewhere to this day. But where? Any wax-coated cardboard Graphophone cylinder of unknown provenance that comes to light in the future must be looked after very carefully, and played only under professional supervision, in case it - and not cylinder number 1929-607 - bears Her Majesty's Voice.

The absence of a label for Sydney's cylinder also mystified me, until I learned that some cylinder collectors in the 1880s and 1890s were in the habit of writing details of their recordings on labels the size of bus tickets. These were slipped inside the cylinders' apertures - and were easily lost when they were removed so that the cylinders could be played. The cylinders were not always kept in tubes or boxes on which a less ephemeral note of their origins could be written. Although Sydney said that his "Queen Victoria" cylinder was his "most cherished possession" and "chiefest treasure", it somehow became unidentifiable towards the end of his life.

Another scenario should also be considered. Sydney is growing old, and the disc playing Gramophone is superseding cylinder players. He finds that his collection of cylinders is no longer of such interest to his friends and relations. He disposes of most of his cylinders, keeping only those that have curiosity or sentimental value. Most of them are Phonograph cylinders; Sydney retains only one Graphophone cylinder, the one on which Queen Victoria had recorded her voice all those years ago - and very different in appearance to the Phonograph cylinder. I don't need to label that one, Sydney decides, its identity is obvious!

Just when I thought that I had considered all the questions surrounding cylinder number 1929-607, my wife asked me: "Can you be sure that when Sydney Morse played the Queen Victoria cylinder in the 1920s he played it at the speed and direction at which it was recorded?" My answer was one that is sometimes given on the television quiz programme Mastermind - "Pass". Having discovered that when the three recordings were made on cylinder number 1929-607, it was rotated at about 100 r.p.m. faster than it should have been and that one of the recordings was made in the opposite direction to the other two, I had to agree that "operator errors could also have been made when the cylinder was played back. Assuming for argument's sake, that cylinder number 1929-607 *is* the one on which Queen Victoria recorded her voice, then it is possible that Sydney Morse unwittingly played it too slowly or too quickly and/or the "wrong way round", to visitors to 14 Airlie Gardens. Many strange and incomprehensible sounds would then have emanated from the cylinder. A woman's voice, distorted in this way, could in places sound more like a man. Sentences played too slowly, or backwards, would bear no resemblance to their true meaning; a word could sound like "tomatoes" but have an entirely different origin.

For the present, this is where the questions, possible answers and speculation must cease. No more can be said on the subject until those in charge of cylinder number 1929-607 and the transcriptions taken from it can initiate more research, such as further processing of Band One and an analysis of the woman's voice. Will the final words on the mystery come from Queen Victoria herself?

APPENDIX I

THE PHONOGRAPH
or
Speaking and Singing Machine

EXTRACTS FROM A LECTURE

DELIVERED BEFORE THE PHYSICAL SOCIETY
by
W.H. PREECE, ESQ.

(Professor ADAMS Presided)

The Phonograph is an instrument which is devised for the reproduction of sound by mechanical means, and it differs from the telephone, inasmuch as the telephone is an instrument that reproduces sound at a distance by electrical means. The phonograph, by its simple definition, evidently means an instrument that reproduces sound at the spot where the sound is itself evolved. But it is not necessarily so, for a portion of the apparatus may be carried to a distance and there be made to reproduce the sounds it has received. For instance, not very long ago, I was asked to call on a gentleman at the Langham Hotel. I went there, and I found upon a table in that gentleman's room an instrument very

similar to that which I have here, and on his turning the
handle the instrument said: "How do you do? How do you like
my phonograph?" Now those words had been spoken by Mr.
Edison, the inventor of the Phonograph, in Menlo Park, New
Jersey, U.S.A. The instrument had been carried across the
Atlantic; it had, for the edification of the passengers on the
steamer, once or twice, or more times, been made to repeat
these words and they were kept intact until they were uttered
for me, for whom they were intended. Thus you see that
although this instrument reproducs sounds on the spot
itself, yet a part of the apparatus can be carried to a distance,
or even on to the uttermost ends of the earth, and will there
reproduce the same sounds at any future time upon a similar
instrument.

Sound is the result of vibrations of matter, and is conveyed
from one spot to another by the pulsations or undulations of
the air that it is in contact with the vibrating matter, and with
our ears. Elastic substances placed in the path of these
sonorous waves take up these vibrations.

It has been said that Lablache, the great bass singer, could
sound a note so deep that it could crack a tumbler; and we
all know that when singing is going on, or any sound is made,
there is a rattling or an indication of vibrations. Now, notes
or sounds of any kind vary in three ways: we have, first of all,
the *pitch* of the note: we have in the second place, the
loudness of the note; and we have in the third place, the
quality of the note. These different properties are due, first,
to the length of the sound waves; secondly, to the amplitude
of those sound waves; and thirdly, to the particular form
which these sound waves take. One of the most remarkable
discoveries of the present age has been the fact that simple

diaphragms like that of the toy telephone can be made to vibrate in numbers amplitude and form, so as to reproduce the human voice.

In the phonograph the first requisite is that we shall have a diaphragm upon which we can speak; and in the instrument before you, which is the phonograph itself, we have, as you see, a simple diaphragm made of very thin iron - the ferrotype that is used so much for telephone experiments. Now, whenever the mouth speaks at a diaphragm, it causes that diaphragm to vibrate, and if to the back of the diaphragm a hard point is fixed clearly that point will move with every vibration of the plates. In front of the diaphragm, which is inside this wood covering, and close to the point in the centre of the diaphragm is fixed a revolving cylinder. This cylinder has a very fine thread cut upon it, which, as arranged, forms a spiral groove along the whole surface of the cylinder. The cylinder has a longitudinal motion, so that the point is passed with uniform motion by the whole length of the spiral groove. Placed upon this cylinder is a sheet of tinfoil. Tinfoil is remarkable in this respect- it is a highly inelastic substance; it very easily yields to any pressure exerted upon it, and, having yielded to that pressure, it retains the form which that pressure may have given it. Now, on a sound being uttered near the diaphragm, the waves of that sound will cause the diaphragm to vibrate, and upon each vibration reaching the diaphragm it causes the point on the latter to press harder against the tinfoil on the cylinder, and an indentation is made. If we make a continuous sound, prolong the vowel "ah" for instance, for a considerable time, then the diaphragm or disc will vibrate the proper number of times to this note, and it will make the proper form of impression to reproduce the quality of this vowel sound.

So that, for the first part of the phonograph, in order to produce some effects by sound, we simply have to speak or sing at the iron diaphragm, which has in connection with it a rotating cylinder covered with a yielding sheet, capable of recording the vibrations imparted by the sounds. The vibrations make very distinct marks upon tinfoil, and having made those marks, which are permanently impressed on the tinfoil, the next duty of the machine is to repeat or reproduce the first vibrations. This is done by simply reversing the whole process. The indentations on the tinfoil now cause the diaphragm again to vibrate and if the rate of motion be the same, the diaphragm will vibrate under the influence of the embossed tinfoil exactly in the same way as it vibrated under the influence of the voice, and it will therefore, give back exactly the same sounds.

We find that musical notes always come out a little clearer than articulate speech, and therefore, though we do not like as a rule to convert a scientific meeting like this into a music-hall entertainment, yet, under the circumstances, I hope you will excuse some wretched music being thrown into this instrument.

The marks that are impressed on the tinfoil by these vibrations are not obliterated, they can be used over and over again, and therefore, just before we put a new tinfoil on the cylinder, we will let the present one run out so that you may have over again the sounds that have been imparted to it.

(This was done)

There is another peculiarity to this instrument, and that is when you have produced on your tinfoil one series of words, it is quite possible to superimpose on these marks a second series, and by this means to bring out at the same time two distinct series of sounds. I have heard two distinct songs sung into this machine and afterwards given out by it with such clearness that by concentrating attention on one or the other either tune could be distinguished, and if two persons spoke into it at the same time, with a little attention, the two distinct voices can be heard; and if it were possible to induce two of this audience who can sing together to sing a duet in the phonograph, the duet would be brought out. I have made a peculiar mouthpiece specially for this purpose. However, I can scarcely hope to venture to hope to induce anybody to do that (if I can so much the better). Here we have one double mouthpiece, one person speaks through one tube and another person through the other, so that by that means we are able to produce two distinct series of sounds at the same time.

To further illustrate the instrument, Mr. Pidgeon here sang a chorus of the war song, "We don't want to fight," &c., cried "Cuckoo", laughed , and cried "Hurrah" three times, which afterwards came out with great clearness on the instrument.

Mr. Sedley Taylor then spoke into the machine - "The Physical Society met on March 2nd to hear the Phonograph," which also came out fairly from the instrument, and caused some amusement. It was tried a second time, but came out rather faintly.

Mr. Preece continuing, said: We will now try the effect of two voices simultaneously, and Mr. Spagnoletti and Mr. Taylor have kindly undertaken to sing "God Save the Queen" (The first four lines were given in tenor and bass, and were afterwards correctly and distinctly intoned by the instrument, although not with very great strength.)

The instrument is, as you will have gathered, one of the great marvels of this marvellous day. It appears that Mr. Edison was experimenting with telephones, a vibrating diaphragm pricked his finger, and the idea of reproducing sound occurred to him one Wednesday afternoon. He set to work. He worked all Wednesday evening, all Wednesday night, all Thursday, all Thursday night, all Friday, all Friday night, and on Saturday morning he succeeded in reproducing sounds as clearly as you have heard in those instruments . He then retired to bed, and slept incessantly from Saturday morning till Monday morning.

APPENDIX II

British Association for the Advancement of Science, Bath Meeting, 1888.

THE GRAPHOPHONE

by

Mr. HENRY EDMUNDS

Nature first gave man the reproduction of his own voice in the echo, and we can imagine his surprise and bewilderment at hearing his words repeated, perchance several times , for who amongst us has not experienced similar surprises: though in this matter-of-fact scientific age, when everything is analysed and explained, much of the charm of mystery is lost. Although echo showed the simplest reproduction of sound, without the aid of vocal organs, or still more complex mechanical devices, such as the puzzled brain of man has devised from time to time, yet it has taken all these years of patient plodding, occasionally assisted by some brilliant accident, to evolve the ultimate but simple device which could repeat these echoes indefinitely, thus surpassing nature in giving back, whenever called upon, the words uttered, storing the same in that fragile but ancient store house, where bees have ever placed their honeyed sweets - in simple wax.

I will now ask you to follow me through the interesting

history of the art of recording and reproducing sound.

One of the Chinese delegation in Washington on seeing the Graphophone, said that they had a legend in China about some fair woman, whose voice was so beautiful, that her children wished to preserve it for future generations to hear; they persuaded her to speak into a bamboo cane, carefully sealing the same. The cane was safely kept for several generations, and then opened at the proper end, when each word came out in order with all the original sweetness, but, unfortunately, could never be repeated.

Leaving this lost art of the Chinese, we come down to more modern times and turning to Professor Tyndall find in his work "On Sound," page 50, in a footnote that "On July 27th, 1681, Mr Hooke showed an experiment making musical and other sounds by the help of the teeth of brass wheels, which teeth were made of equal bigness for musical sounds but of unequal for vocal". (See *Birch's History of the Royal Society*, page 96, published in the year 1757).

In addition to this, I would quote the following extract from the life of Dr Hooke, which precedes his posthumous work, published in 1705, by Richard Waller, the Secretary of the Royal Society:

> In July the same year, he (Dr Hooke) showed a way of making musical and other sounds by the striking the teeth of several brass wheels, proportionally cut as to their numbers, and turned very fast round, in which it was observable that the equal proportionate strokes of the teeth made musical notes, but the unequal strokes of the teeth more resembled the sound of the voice in speaking".

It is remarkable that these notices were published in 1705 and 1757, while the experiments themselves were made in 1681, over 200 years ago, and yet the idea of simply mechanically reproducing the human voice has lain dormant all these years.

In 1854, Charles Bourseuil advanced the idea that two diaphragms, one operating an electric contact, and the other under the influence of an electro magnet, might be employed for transmitting speech over telegraphic distance, "Speak against one diaphragm," he said, "and let each vibration break or make the electric contact, and the electric pulsations thereby produced will set the other diaphragm vibrating, and the latter ought then to reproduce the transmitted sound."

In 1857, the phonatograph was patented in France by Leon Scott. It had for its purpose of recording the sound vibrations upon a cylinder rotated by hand and moved forward by a screw. The cylinder was covered with paper, which was smoked over a flame, and a stylus attached to the centre of a diaphragm, under the influence of words spoken into a large barrel-like mouthpiece, would trace sound vibrations upon the smoked surface. But no attempt was made at reproducing sounds.

In 1859, Philip Reis actually made an apparatus, such as indicated by Bourseuil, which is now known as the Reis telephone.

Faber also attempted to construct a talking machine, after the system of the human organs of speech, a mass of intricate mechanism, levers, bellows and pulleys, which gave unearthly utterances of a few words and sentences.

But the Bell telephone came in 1876 - it taught how a simple piece of apparatus could produce perfect results, and, that any diaphragm, however thick, could be made to set up audible articulate vibrations.

On the 30th day of April 1877, M. Charles Cros deposited with the Secretary of the Academy of Sciences in Paris a sealed envelope, containing a paper on a:

"PROCESS OF RECORDING AND OF REPRODUCING
AUDIBLE PHENOMENA"

which, in translation is as follows:-

"In general, my process consists in obtaining the tracing of the to-and-fro movements of a vibrating membrane, and the utilization of this tracing for reproducing the same to-and-fro movement, with their relative inherent durations and intensities in the same membrane, or in another adapted for the furnishing the sounds and noises which result from this series of movements.

"We are, therefore, concerned with the transformation of an extremely delicate tracing, such as that obtained with a delicate stylus rubbing upon a surface blackened by a flame, to transform, I say, these tracings in relief or intaglio, in resisting material capable of guiding a moving body which transmits these movements to a sonorous membrane.

"A light stylus is connected with the centre of a vibrating membrane; it terminates in a point (metallic wire, the barb of a feather, etc.), which bears upon a surface blackened by a flame. This surface is part of a disc to which is given a double movement of rotation and rectilinear progression.

"If the membrane is at rest, the point will trace a simple spiral; if the membrane vibrates, the traced spiral will be undulating, and these undulations represent exactly all the to-and-fro movements of the membrane, with their times and intensities."

Up to this point the apparatus as described would represent a modified Scott phonatograph, in which the cylinder is replaced by a flat disc. M. Cros then continues:-

"By means of the photographic process which, in fact, is well known, this traced, transparent, undulatory spiral is converted into a line of similar dimensions, in intaglio or in relief, in resisting material like tempered steel, for instance.

"This done, this resisting surface is, by means of a motor apparatus, made to turn and to progress rectilinearly with a velocity like that which was used in the registration.

"If the reproduced tracing is in intaglio, a metallic point (and if it is in relief, a notched finger), held by a spring, bears up on the tracing at one end, and is connected at the other end with the centre of the membrane adapted for sound reproduction. Under these conditions, this membrane is not any more acted upon by the vibrating air, but by the tracing, controlling the pointed stylus by pulsations exactly like those to which the membrane was subjected in recording, both as to duration and intensity."

This paper was only read in open session at the Academy on December 3rd 1877, *nevertheless to Charles Cros belongs the honour of having first suggested the idea of, and feasible plan for mechanically reproducing speech once uttered*. But meanwhile Mr T. A. Edison appeared with the Phonograph.

I believe I had the honour of being one of the first Englishmen to see this instrument, as in 1877, I was in the United States, observing the scientific progress of the period, visiting different institutions, and meeting various professors and inventors: amongst others, I saw Mr Edison in November of that year.

From what I learnt by published reports, Mr Edison, sometime in the latter part of September that year, was at work on an automatic telephone by which he intended to impress a telephone message, on a strip of tinfoil, and let the indentations thereby produced act upon a variable resistance, such as a lampblack button, and thereby transmit the message over the wire. While one day at work upon this, so the report runs, he accidentally passed the previously indented slip under the recording stylus which, as in the Scott Phonatograph, was connected to the centre of a diaphragm, and there occurred the first actual reproduction by mechanical means of words registered before.

The Phonograph became then, at once, an accomplished fact, for to such an experienced inventor it took but a short time to cover the cylinder of a Scott Phonatograph with tinfoil, and to indent the same at right angles to the surface of the cylinder.

I was much interested in it, and returning to England in

December 1877, sent in a full report to the London *Times*, which appeared in their issue of the 17th February, 1878. Shortly afterwards, the first Phonograph made in this country by Mr Stroh, under my instructions, was exhibited by Mr W. H. Preece, the President of this Section, at his interesting lecture at the Royal Institution. This was the first public exhibition of the "Edison Phonograph" or sound recording machine in this country.

Everybody remembers the sensation which the invention produced, and the prognostications which were advanced for it by the scientific press showed that the principle of the apparatus was considered to contain the germ of an ultimate achievement of the most accurate result; but that it left something to be desired may be judged from the following lines sent to me by Mr Perry F. Nursey after hearing the instrument on February 27th 1878:-

LINES ON HEARING THE PHONOGRAPH

How, Adam, Noah, Melchisedie,
    And all their friends would laugh,
Could they but visit earth again,
    And hear the Phonograph.

Sure Memnon, son of morning's voice,
    Could not be more melodious,
Nor could old Stantor's roaring lungs
    E'er utter sounds more odious.

The former's smooth as brooklet flows,
    The latter's harsh as medicine,
But smooth or rough, like honour goes,
    To Thomas Alva Edison.

Great things were expected of this instrument, and a large company was formed in America called the "Edison Phonograph Company". It was proposed to record speech mechanically, in place of employing stenographers; to attach phonographs to clocks which could call out the time of day or night, instead of striking bells, and, in fact, and in fact, all kinds of proposals were made, as to various applications on the assumption that tinfoil could be indented by the human voice and that such indentation would intelligibly reproduce articulate speech. But what was the actual result? A few instruments were made for exhibition, but none were made use of for any practical purpose. The human voice might speak into the instrument, but only a caricature of it was reproduced, and the ultimate result may be best described in Mr Edison's own words, in a characteristic interview in the *New York World*, afterwards copied into the *Electrical World* of Nov. 12, 1887:-

> "It weighed about 100 pounds; it cost a mint of money to make; no one but an expert could get anything intelligible back from it, the record made by the little steel point upon a sheet of tinfoil lasted but a few times after it had been put through the Phonograph. I myself doubted whether I should ever see a perfect Phonograph ready to record any kind of ordinary speech, and to give it out again intelligibly. But was be perfectly sure if we did not accomplish this the next generation would. And I dropped the Phonograph and went to work upon the Electric Light"

Such an instrument I had given to me by Mr Edison in 1879.

But fortunately, the subject was not abandoned by others.

In the spring of 1881, a special arrangement was made between Professor Alexander Graham Bell; the inventor of the Telephone, Dr Chichester A. Bell and Charles Sumner Tainter, resulting in the formation of the Volta Laboratory Association, so called after the Volta Prize of 50,000f, awarded to Prof. Bell by the French Government for the invention of the Telephone, which sum he thus devoted to scientific research, and the study and elaboration of ideas, inventions, and discoveries relating to the art of transmitting, recording and reproducing sounds, and in Mr Tainter's own words:-

> "We began work in this direction by studying the causes of the failure of the Phonograph. We saw that its construction was not in the first place adapted to produce in the metal foil an exact record of the sonorous vibrations: since, owing to the pliability of the material, the action of the stylus, while forming the record, has a tendency to alter and distort the portion immediately back of the point of action. Another cause of inaccuracy was due to the action of the reproducing dia-phragm, which, while acted upon positively by the stylus in one direction, that is, when the latter was raised by elevation in the record, had to re-act by its elasticity in the other. Furthermore, it was very evident that an instrument forming a record in a pliable strip could never be practically suc-cessful, since the record was essentially perish-able. The utmost care was necessary in handling it to prevent injury, and every attempt at repro-duction tended to smooth out and obliterate the sound record.

"It became evident, therefore, at the outset, that the methods of indenting a pliable strip, whether of tinfoil, or of paper saturated with wax or a similar composition, involved elements of failure that could not be eliminated; that it would be useless to attempt improving the phonograph, and that an entirely different mode of recording, in a substance not possessing the detrimental properties of the pliable strip or sheet, must be discovered. We immediately addressed ourselves to that discovery and its practical embodiment.

" From the experience we had with the pliable strip, we soon determined that the record to be permanent, must be produced on a plate of solid resisting material.

"Amongst the new methods proposed by us for forming the undulatory record, that regarded with the most favour was to engrave the record directly in a solid material with a cutting style adapted to grave or gouge out the material acted upon, thus forming the groove, the bottom of which presented irregularities constituting the sound record.

"One of the main difficulties with the original phonograph was its indistinctness of articulation. While giving a loud sound, it was utterly impossible to reproduce intelligible speech, and for that reason in exhibiting the instrument, experiments were confined to recording familiar nursery rhymes and songs which the ear could recognise from the rhythm.

"We found in the course of our experiments, that while records cut in wax were much more perfect than those indented in metal foil, greater distinctness could also be gained by reducing the size of the record and concentrating the sound by hearing tubes in the listener's ear. Thus a double advantage was gained; for, besides the vastly improved articulation, privacy in the use of the instruments was ensured. A number of instruments could utter their distinct messages in each listener's ear without mutual disturbance; and the overhearing of private communications was prevented"

The work at the laboratory was continued with great assiduity for 4 years when in May, 1885, the Association was dissolved by mutual consent. During the time a number of valuable inventions and discoveries had been worked out and perfected, and many patents (all in force) were taken out both in the United States and abroad in connection with this subject, the following claims: among others, being granted:-

"The method of forming a record of sounds by impressing sonorous vibration upon a style, and thereby cutting in a solid body the record corresponding in form to the sound waves, in contradistinction to the formation of sound records by indenting a foil with a vibratory style etc.

"The vibratory *cutting* style of a sound recorder.

"A sound record consisting of a tablet, or other solid body, having its surface *cut or engraved* with narrow lines of irregular and varied forms, corresponding to sound waves.

"The method of forming a sound or speech record, which consists in engraving or cutting the same in wax, or a wax-like composition."

The instrument termed the Graphophone was the final result of these labours, and to these gentlemen belongs the honour of producing the first practical speaking machine brought before the public, and of demonstrating the difference between indentations, and continuous engraving, analagous to the difference between the imperfect Reis transmitter and the perfect-speaking of the Bell Telephone.

Mr Tainter informs me that a Graphophone was privately shown to one of Mr Edison's associates in Washington in July 1885. As a result of this examination, with a view to making a commercial working arrangement, it was taken to New York in August, and shown privately to some members of the Edison Phonograph Company, but nothing came of the negotiations.

The instrument was illustrated and described in an article in *Harper's Weekly* of July 17th, 1886.

We will now review the English Patent Office between 1877 and 1886, thus gauging somewhat the work of inventors in this field.

No.2909 - July 30th 1877. T. A. Edison

In this specification, among other things, it was proposed to obtain a record of vocal and other sounds by causing the movements of a diaphragm to be registered on chemically prepared paper or soft metal, and to use this paper or metal, to reproduce the sounds by acting on a diaphragm. (The claims relating to this part of the invention were abandoned by a disclaimer, filed August 17, 1882.)

4847. Dec 20th 1877. McEvoy

This specification relates to the construction of telephones, and refers to a diagram showing the telephone combined with phonograph, but gives no particulars as to the construction of the latter.

(patent void)

4934 December 29th 1877. C. W. Harrison

This invention relates to electric telephones, and the inventor states that a record of sounds may be obtained by taking the current through the coils of an electro magnet carrying a point on its armature to indent a movable surface.

(patent void)

1664 April 24th, 1878 T. A. Edison (patent void)

Here Mr Edison proposes a backing of wax, or yielding material, instead of a grooved surface, in order to support the metal foil which receives the *indentation*.

The term *indenting*, as used by Mr Edison throughout his patent specifications, clearly means the action of *embossing* the material without the removal of any part of it, as in forming a record in tinfoil by pressing upon it with a style.

But that he did not believe in the practicability of his Phonograph is shown by the fact that this patent was allowed to lapse on April 24th, 1885, in consequence of non-payment of a £100 fee, just at the period of the completion of the experiments of the Volta Laboratory Association.

3129 July 18th, 1881. J. J. Walker

This Provisional Specification states that a perforated band is caused to travel past an orifice through which a stream of air issues. The perforated band may be produced from a photograph taken upon a moving surface of an edge caused to vibrate by the voice or sound to be reproduced, or a strip produced by a phonograph may be employed.

(No patent)

291 January 20th 1882. J. D. Morel of France

This provisional Specification describes a phonograph in which a travelling band of paper, etc. is employed. The band may be of blotting paper drawn through a gelatinous bath.

(No patent)

7926 May 19th, 1884 A. F. St George

A plumbago pencil attached to a diaphragm makes a line of varying distinctness on a travelling surface. To reproduce the sounds, the plumbago line is drawn between two terminals of an electric current, and produces undulations in the current corresponding to the variations in the line produced by the pencil.

(Patent void)

Then we come to the existing Volta Laboratory Patents of 4th May 1886, which, among other things, cover the method of *cutting* in a solid body, a record corresponding to the sound waves, in contra distinction to the formation of sound records by *indenting* a foil with a vibratory style. The vibratory *cutting* style of a sound recorder. The sound record consisting of a tablet or other solid body having its surface *cut or engraved* with narrow lines. And the method of *engraving* or *cutting* the same in wax, or a wax-like composition.

May 4th 1886 No 6027

"Improvements in and Apparatus for Recording and Reproducing Speech and other Sounds."

May 4th 1886 No 6042

"Improvements in and Apparatus for Reproducing Sound from Phonographic Records."

May 4th 1886 No 6047

"Improvements in and Means and Apparatus for the Reproduction of Speech and other Sounds by Means of Records."

May 4th 1886 No 6062

"Transmitting and Recording Sounds by means of radiant energy and means and Apparatus therefor"

Now, it is remarkable that between 1877, when Edison's Phonograph was described, and 1886, when the Volta Laboratory patents were published, only these five patents were applied for in this line of work, (although in telephone, and other kindred subjects, the patents might be numbered by the hundreds.); and all of these five patents were abandoned, including Mr Edison's, before the Volta Laboratory Association took out theirs, which are now in force. But we find that since 1886, in addition to their own, more than seventeen new patents have been applied for by other inventors in connection with this subject; all tending to show that the researches of the Volta Laboratory Association had ended in a complete success for all practical purposes. That this was the fact is best proved by the adoption, by Mr Edison, of their wax cylinder, and graving out process, in contradistinction to the tinfoil slip and indenting style, which had been found to be useless in practice. Therefore, it is no wonder that Mr Emile Berliner states, in his interesting paper read before the Franklin Institute at Philadelphia, on the Gramophone, May

16th 1888, that the new Edison Phonograph and the Tainter-Bell Graphophone appear to be practically the same apparatus, differing only in form and motive power. As mentioned above, the Graphophone was shown to Mr Edison's associates in 1885, and the Volta Patents were granted in 1886, but it was not until 1888 that Mr Edison's Phonograph reappeared, and all the praise accorded to Mr Edison and his agents for the "improved Phonograph" is fairly due to Mr Charles Sumner Tainter, and his associates in the Volta Laboratory Association.

The Graphophone as shown here is propelled mechanically. The whole has been designed to attain the best results with the fewest parts and absence of skilled attention. There is no electricity. An ordinary treadle like a sewing machine, rotates a speed governor. This by a leather belt communicates a constant speed to the rotating wax cylinder. A diaphragm of mica carrying a steel graver, called the recorder, is mounted in a metal holder, (which, by means of a revolving screw) traverses the wax cylinder, cutting a fine thread 160 to the inch, a mouthpiece attached to a flexible tube carries the sound vibrations to the diaphragm which causes the graver or style to cut into the wax a series of depressions more or less frequent, and varying in depth according to the sounds producing the vibrations. These undulations, while so slight as to be scarcely perceptible, can, nevertheless, produce in the diaphragm of the reproducer similar vibrations to the original sounds and give back, not once, but indefinitely, the words or sounds which were first recorded. The instrument can be instantly stopped or started at any time, whether recording or reproducing, by simply pressing the button with the finger. No adjustments are required by the user; the recorder and reproducer being mounted flexibly and so adapting themselves to any eccentricities of the wax cylinder. This is especially useful in the reproduction of damaged cylinders. I had an instance recently where one came to me through the post, having been opened and crushed. Nevertheless the delicate reproducer, with its flexible mountings was able to follow the original record, and reproduce every word distinctly. Great economy has been found in the use of a cardboard cylinder coated with wax instead of solid wax cylinders. They are more easily handled, less liable to fracture, and much lighter for postage, besides being cheaper than notepaper, when the saving in time in writing is considered.

The very simplicity of the instrument startles us - but who shall say what its future may be - and what revolutions it may effect. Its introduction into everyday life marks a new era. Truly the unlimited reproduction of the human voice in speech and song is a most wonderful achievement. When we consider its marvellous adaptability to modern life, there seems to be no limit to its powers. A child may work it and communicate to those who love it, its childish prattle; or preserving the small cylinder refer in after life to how it spoke. Business men may carry on negotiations, recording each word spoken, preventing misunderstandings as to what was said. Attached to the telephone, even the fleeting words that be recorded for future reference [sic]. The stenographer may read his notes to it, leaving it to dictate to others to write them out And Tennyson's wish for the voice that is still, be realized at last.

I cannot conclude better than quoting an impromptu, spoken into the Graphophone at Washington, in July this

year by Colonel Joyce: a piece which repeated itself to me as
follows: -

I treasure the voices of poets and sages,
I keep them alive through the round rolling years;
I speak to the world for ages and ages,
Recording the language of smiles and of tears,

When friends have departed, and sweet life has ended,
Their voices shall sound through my swift rolling heart:
While all of their love-notes are treasured and blended,
As faithful and true as the nature of art.

The pulpit, the bar, the wants of the household,
Shall photograph thought in the sigh of my soul:
The man and maid shall advance more than tenfold,
Who talk with my tongue as the years grandly roll.

The Godhead alone shall be found in my preaching,
And marvellous secrets I yet shall disclose.
The schools of the world shall list to my teaching,
As pure and as bright as the blush of the rose.

I war with the world where ignorance slumbers,
And go hand in hand with the light of the sun,
I count every thought with quick magical numbers;
And my work on the earth shall never be done.

CHRONOLOGY

1877

April: Charles Cros writes a paper describing the process of recording and reproducing sound and on April 18th and deposits it with Academie des Sciences on April 30th.

June 22nd: Henry Edmunds sails for America.

July: Thomas Edison begins experiments with sound recording,

November/December: Edison sketches apparatus on November 29th, construction is completed by December 6th, Edmunds is present at the experiment at the laboratory.

December 22nd: Edison demonstrates his tinfoil Phonograph for the *Scientific American* magazine.

1878

January: Henry Edmunds sets up business as an electrical engineer in London; helps to build the first British Phonograph.

February 1st: William Preece delivers the first lecture in Britain on the Phonograph, demonstrating the first British-built machine.

February 27th: Preece delivers lecture on the Phonograph to the Society of Telegraph Engineers.

March 2nd: Preece delivers lecture on the Phonograph to the Physical Society.

1880

Alexander Graham Bell sets up the Volta Laboratory in Washington, DC with Chichester Bell and Charles Sumner Tainter.

1881

October 20th: the Bells and Tainter deposit a Graphophone, at the Smithsonian Institution.

1885

June 27th: Bell and Tainter apply for patents for the Graphophone.

1886

May 7th: Patents for the Graphophone granted.

1887

August: Henry Edmunds visits the U.S.A. and is appointed European Representative by Volta Laboratories to promote the Graphophone.

1888

June 16th: Edison introduces the Improved Phonograph.

September: Edmunds and Walter Twiss Glover set up the Graphophone agency.

September 6th: Henry Edmunds and Colonel Gouraud demonstrate the Graphophone and the "Perfected Phonograph" at the Masonic Hall, Bath.

Autumn: Gouraud records the voices of William Gladstone, Lord Tennyson and Robert Browning on the Phonograph.

Sydney Morse visits Balmoral and records Queen Victoria on the Graphophone.

1898

August 8th; Queen Victoria makes a recording on a Phonograph and the cylinder is sent to Emperor Menelik of Abyssinia: this recording is subsequently destroyed.

1907

March: Sydney Morse dines with Princess Louise and attempts to play the Queen Victoria recording.

1922

Sydney Morse plays the "Queen Victoria Recording" to his grandchildren at his London home.

1927

November 18th: death of Henry Edmunds.

1929

January: death of Sydney Morse.

May 16th: Esmond Morse offers the family's Graphophone and recordings to the Science Museum.

June 22nd: Graphophone cylinder accepted by the Science Museum.

1964

October: Lord Tangley, of Sydney Morse and Co., attempts to trace the whereabouts of the "Queen Victoria cylinder".

1965

February; Lord Tangley abandons search.

1980

October: Sydney Morse's Graphophone cylinder correctly identified in Science Museum inventory.

1991

June 11th: Morse's cylinder played at the National Sound Archive.

FURTHER READING

Collecting Phonographs and Gramophones: Christopher Proudfoot, 1980.

Discography of Historical Records on Cylinders and 78s: Brian Rust, 1979.

Edison - a Biography: Matthew Josephson, 1959.

The Edison Cylinder Phonographs, 1877 - 1929: George L .Frow and Albert F. Sefl, 1978.

Edison, the Man who Made the Future: Ronald W Clark, 1977.

Edison Phonograph - the British Connection: Frank Andrews, 1987.

The Fabulous Phonograph (2nd Edition): Roland Gelatt, 1977.

From Tinfoil to Stereo (2nd Edition): Oliver Read and Walter L. Welch, 1976.

Talking Machines (2nd Edition): V. K. Chew, 1981.

ACKNOWLEDGEMENTS

Many people gave me valuable assistance while I was writing this book. My special thanks to Charles Ainley, Mary Barton, Lord Montagu of Beaulieu, Benet Bergonzi, Peter Copeland, Cicely Edmunds, Philip English, John Hay, John Holgate, Diana Holman-Hunt, the Countess of Longford, Stephanie Millard, David Morse, Dr Michael Pritchard, Christopher Proundfoot, Dr Derek Robinson, Leonard and Voilet Simmonds.

Mr H.A. Mavor of Anderson Strathclyde Ltd and several descendants and relatives of Henry Edmunds provided copies of photographs. Some of these are reproduced here; others will appear in my forthcoming biography of Henry Edmunds. Other relatives passed on vital information or sent me copies of letters and documents, all of which filled gaps in my knowledge of Henry's activities as a promoter of sound recording apparatus.

Michael Worthington-Williams, the motoring historian and journalist, and Michael Ware, curator of the National Motor Museum at Beaulieu, offered helpful advice when I was seeking a publisher. Tony Freeman of Academy Books has supported me enthusiastically ever since he read the synopsis of my biography of Henry Edmunds in the spring of 1991. Thanks to his advice and skill as my publisher and editor, my Henry Edmunds project developed into two books, whereas originally I had intended to write only one!

I was delighted that George Frow, who is such a respected authority on early recording machines, accepted my invitation to write the Foreword. Eight years previously, George had given me useful guidance on how to survive New York's PATH subway and the Erie-Lackawanna Railroad, when my research necessitated a visit to the Edison National Historic Site at West Orange, New Jersey.

My thanks also to those who read the first draft of my manuscript and put forward constructive comments and suggestions. Any errors of fact or interpretation are, of course, entirely my own responsibility.

Investigating Henry Edmunds's connections with the Phonograph and the Tainter-Bell Graphophone, and searching for the 'Queen Victoria' recording cylinder, were fascinating and demanding tasks, and I would have overlooked many important details had I not benefited from information given by those mentioned in the foregoing chapters and also by Frank Andrews (City of London Phonograph and Gramophone Society); Gordon Bruce; L. Cohen (Institute of Physics, London); the Royal Society of Arts; Mrs I.M. McCabe (The Royal Institution); Mrs Leah S. Burt (Edison National Historic Site); Jane Langton (Royal Archives); Dr D.W. Morley, Sarah Willcox (British Association for the Advancement of Science) and Robert Long (*High Fidelity* magazine, Great Barrington, Massachusetts).

My wife Pat became a 'book widow' for many weekends while I neglected family and domestic responsibilities and became preoccupied with my research and with writing the manuscript. My project could not have been completed on time without Pat's invaluable assistance at the word processor, and her assistance while I was collecting and collating the illustrations, checking the proofs and compiling the index.

My thanks also to Timothy Auty; David Arscott, Robert Gunnell (BBC Radio Brighton, now BBC Radio Sussex); Margaret Cox (BBC Sound Archives); Ronald W. Clark; Roland Gelatt; Brian Butler, John Hargreaves, D.M. Hallowes (Halifax Antiquarian Society); Mrs E.D.P. Symons (The Institution of Electrical Engineers); Mr W.A. Morris (The Institution of Civil Engineers); Larry E. Sullivan (New York Historical Society); Dr Richard Hills, Christine Heap (North Western Museum of Science and Industry, Manchester); Lord Ponsonby of Shulbrede; Francis James Dallett (University of Pennsylvania); Rex King (The Rugby Football Union); Christine Lamar, Marie F. Harper (Rhode Island Historical Society); Roy Russell; John Physick (Victoria & Albert Museum).

THE AUTHOR

Paul Tritton was born in Canterbury, England, and began his writing career in the 1950s, as a newspaper reporter in Kent and Dorset. For the past 30 years he has worked as an industrial PR executive and consultant. He spends his spare time researching the histories of business enterprises and writing about the achievements of pioneers in engineering and transport. He is especially interested in the Victorian and Edwardian eras.

Paul contributes to various special-interest journals. He has won two awards from the British Association of Industrial Editors - a Certificate of Merit for an article on the autogyro pioneer Wing Commander Kenneth Wallis, and the Shell Mex & BP Trophy for an article on the men and women who built Rolls-Royce Merlin aero-engines in World War II. His first book, 'John Montagu of Beaulieu - motoring prophet and pioneer,' won the Society of Automotive Historians's 1986 Award of Distinction.

INDEX

Other titles available from Academy Books:

Transport

	£
Lanchester Cars, 1895-1956 (Freeman, Long & Hood)	11.95
Daimler and Lanchester, An Illustrated History (Freeman)	19.95
Humber, An Illustrated History, 1868-1976 (Freeman)	14.95
Post-War Standard Cars (Freeman, Long & Hood)	9.95
Pre-War Standard Cars (Long & Freeman)	10.95
High Performance Cortinas (Davis)	19.95
How to Trace the History of Your Car (Riden)	3.95

Motor Sport

Star Cars of the Ovals (Ruston)	9.95

Local History

Incident Closed -A History of the Fire Service in Coventry	6.95
A History of Monmouthshire (Bradney) (9 part set)	
Vol 1, Part 1: The Hundred of Skenfrith	14.95
Vol 1, Part 2a: Abergavenny Hundred	14.95
Vol 1, Part 2b: Abergavenny Hundred (due February 92)	19.95
Vol 2, Part 1: Raglan Hundred (due April 92)	14.95
Vol 2, Part 2: Trelech Hundred (due June 92)	14.95
Vol 3, Part 1: Usk Hundred (due August 92)	12.95
Vol 3, Part 2: Usk Hundred (due October 92)	19.95
Vol 4, Part 1: Usk Hundred (due December 92)	14.95
Vol 4, Part 2: Usk Hundred (due February 93)	19.95

Biography

The Godfather of Rolls-Royce (Paul Tritton)

The life and times of Henry Edmunds, entrepreneur, inventor and motoring pioneer, who introduced Charles Rolls to Henry Royce and played a key part in the development of the early Rolls-Royce company. This is fascinating biography of a man at the forefront of technological developments at the turn of the century. (Due March 1992).   £14.95

Orders to:
Academy Books Limited,
35 Pretoria Avenue,
London E17 7DR

Telephone: 081 521 7647 Facsimile: 081 503 6655.
Please allow £2.75 (UK) £5.50 (o'seas) for postage and packing
All major credit cards accepted by telephone, post or fax.

BIRKBECK COLLEGE
Malet Street, London WC1E 7HX
020 7631 6239
If not previously recalled for another reader,
this book should be returned or renewed
before the latest date stamped below.